Daily Mail

MINDBENDER
PUZZLES

Daily Mail

MINDBENDER PUZZLES

Dave Colton

Bounty Books

First published
by Headline Book Publishing
as *Daily Mail Mindbender Puzzles Volume 1 (2001),*
Daily Mail Mindbender Puzzles Volume 2 (2001)
and *Daily Mail Mindbender Puzzles Volume 3 (2002)*

This edition published 2005 by Bounty Books,
a division of Octopus Publishing Group Ltd
2-4 Heron Quays, London E14 4JP
Reprinted in 2007

ISBN 13 : 978-0-7537-13-33-4
ISBN 10 : 0-7537 13-33-0

A CIP catalogue record for this book is available
from the British Library

Printed and bound in Great Britain

Part 1

1

Add the vowels to the consonants to discover a well-known saying.

2

Take one letter from each circle to spell out the name of a festive occasion.

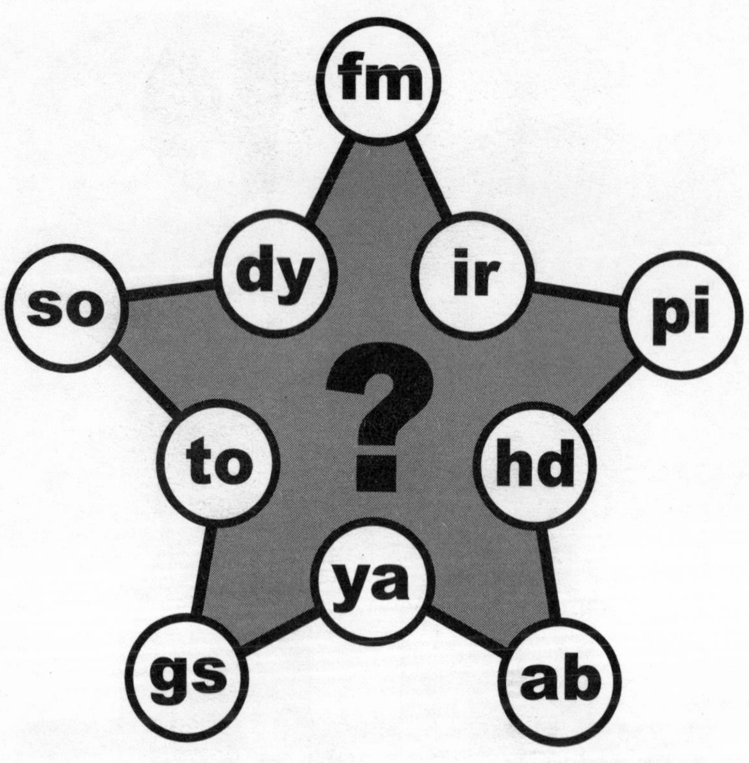

3

Which of these is the odd one out?

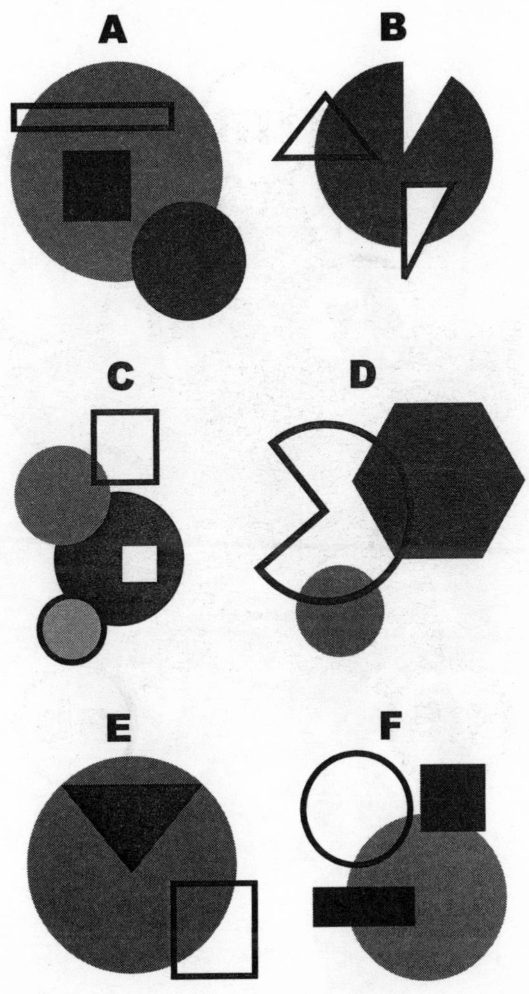

4

Find the letters missing from this alphabet, then arrange them into the name of a famous person.

5

A major chain of shops has recently slashed the prices of a range of goods.

How much have they reduced the price of the skateboard?

6

Which of the symbols below is missing from this sequence?

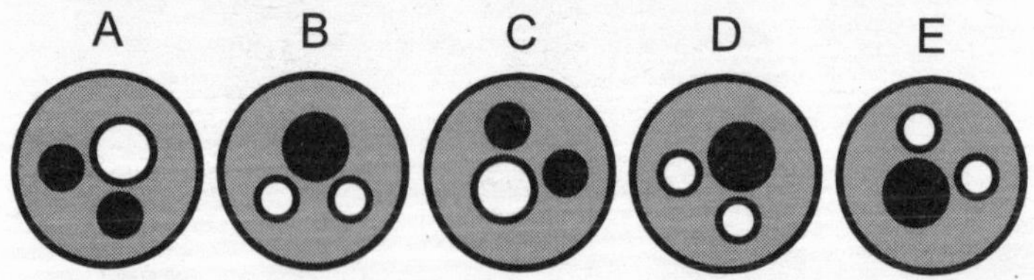

7

If the fork is worth three more than seventy and the knife half of six, what is the value of the spoon?

8

The Raymond, Smith and Jackson families have all lived in this road for nine years.

How long have the O'Neil family lived here?

9

Find five mistakes in this pattern.

10

Can you discover Jane Smith's favourite wine from the code below?

11

Ian's favourite meal is pizza and his preferred drink is tea. He works in London and owns a timeshare in Spain.

Does he drive a BMW or a Rover?

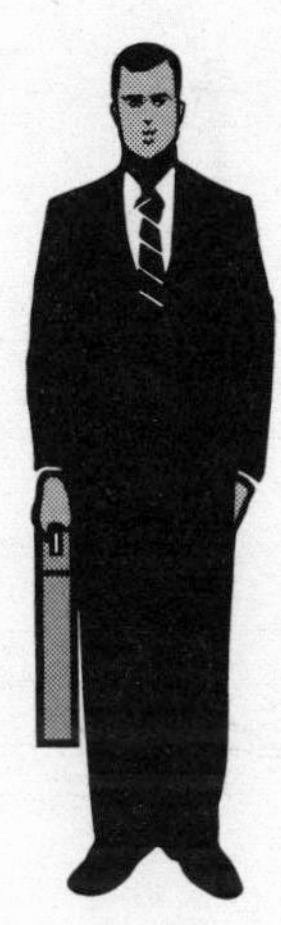

12

Which shape should replace the question mark in this sequence?

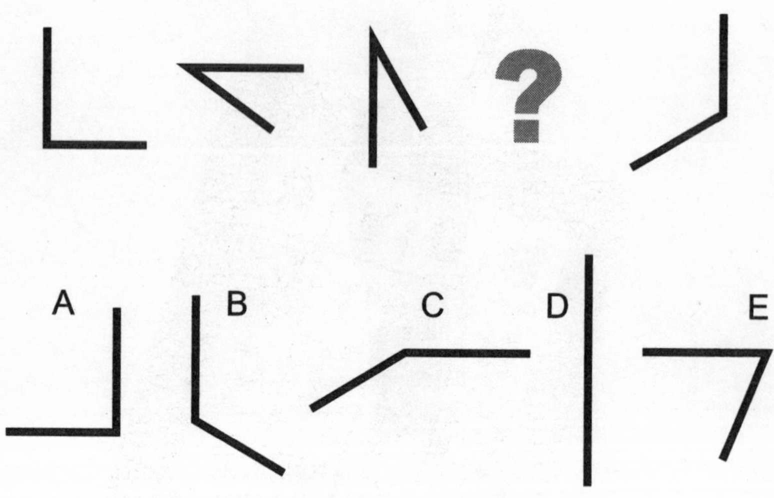

13

What are the two missing letters on this keypad?

14

Which shape is the odd one out?

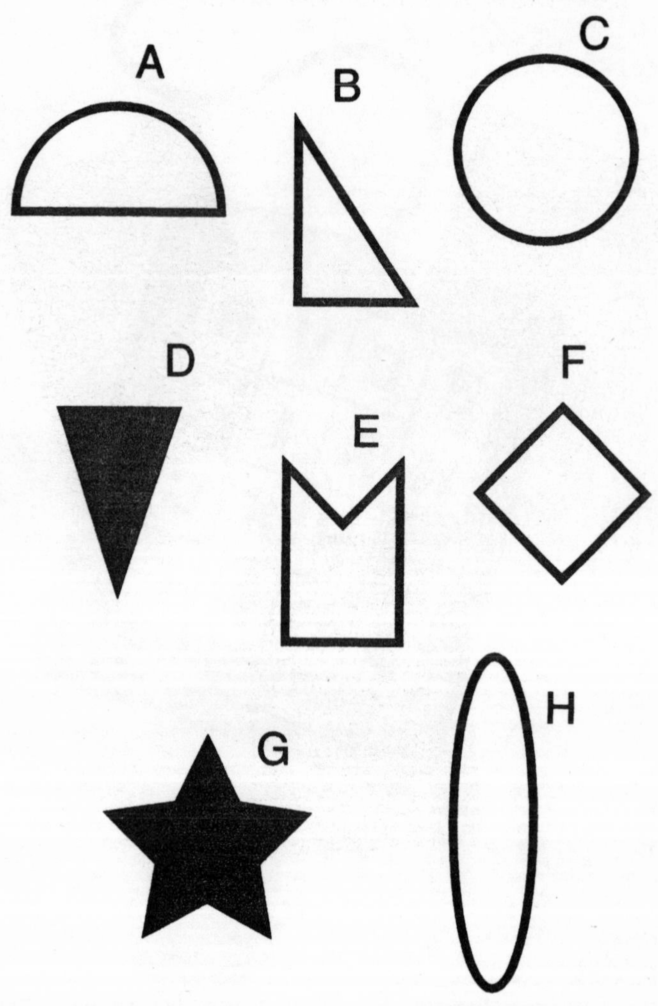

15

In a city this month the following crimes have been committed.

How many assaults were there?

16

Which is the odd one out?

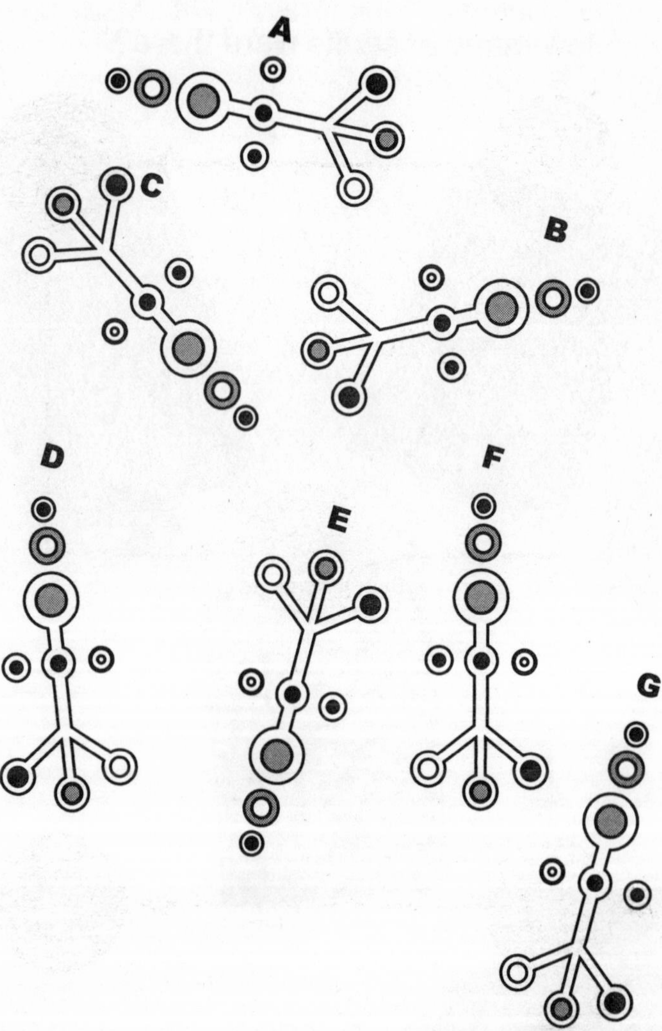

17

Which letter is missing?

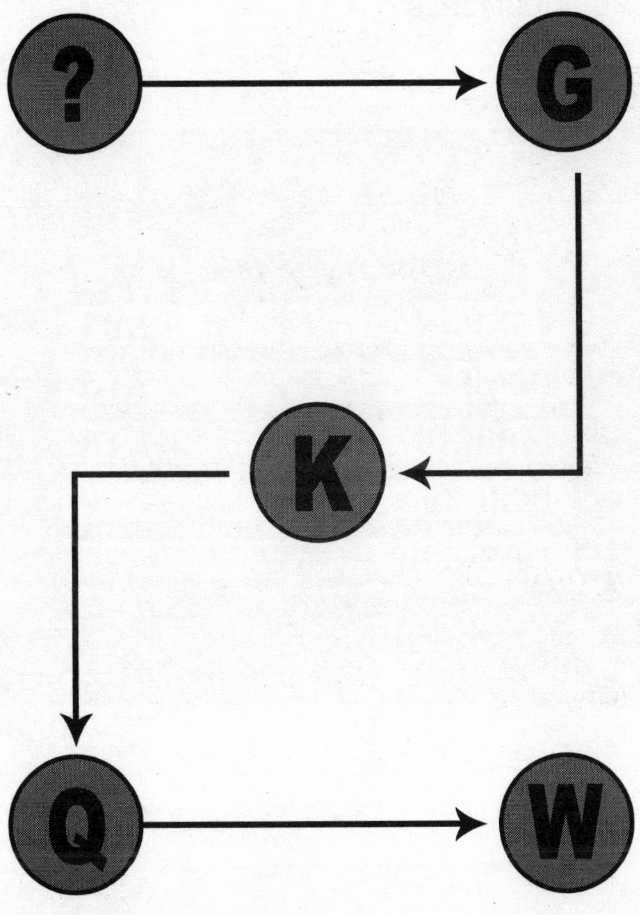

18

Here are some departure times of flights from Manchester airport.

What time do the flights to Berlin and Istanbul leave?

DEPARTURES

LONDON	14.04
ROME	15.13
MADRID	04.18
BERLIN	-- --
ISTANBUL	-- --

19

Here are the number of bookings a restaurant has for next week.

How many do they have on Wednesday?

20

Crack the code to discover the film title.

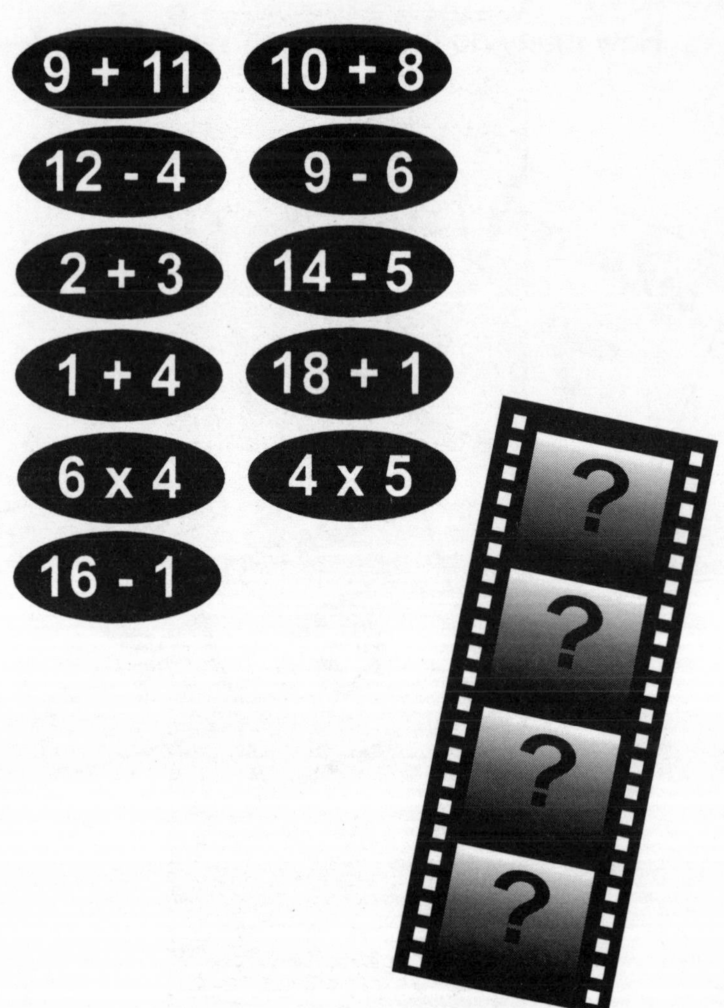

21

Can you find ten differences between these two boxes?

Replace the missing block.

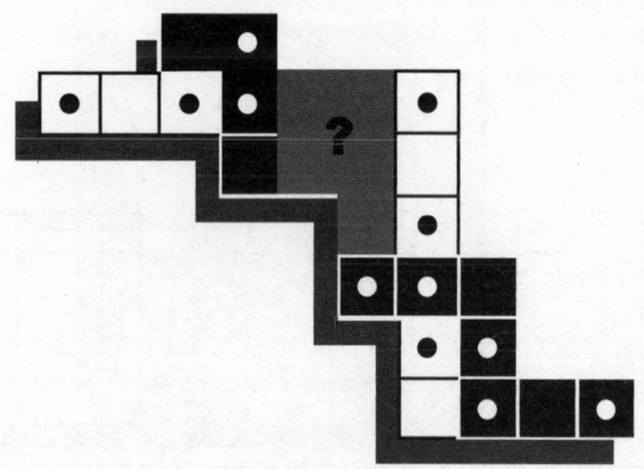

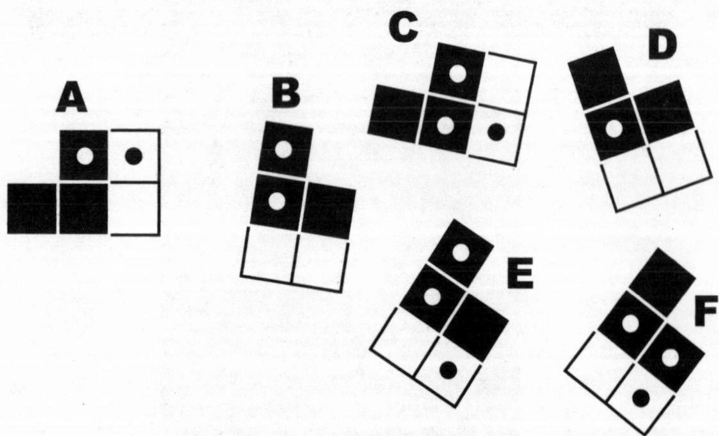

23

Where should the black spot be in the last grid?

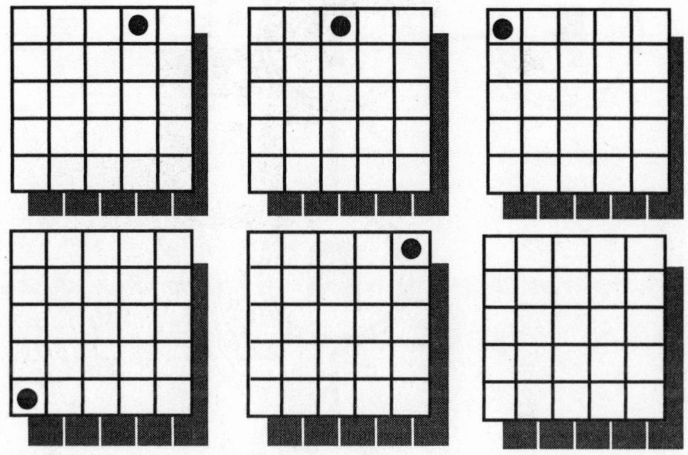

24

Which two letters are missing from this sequence?

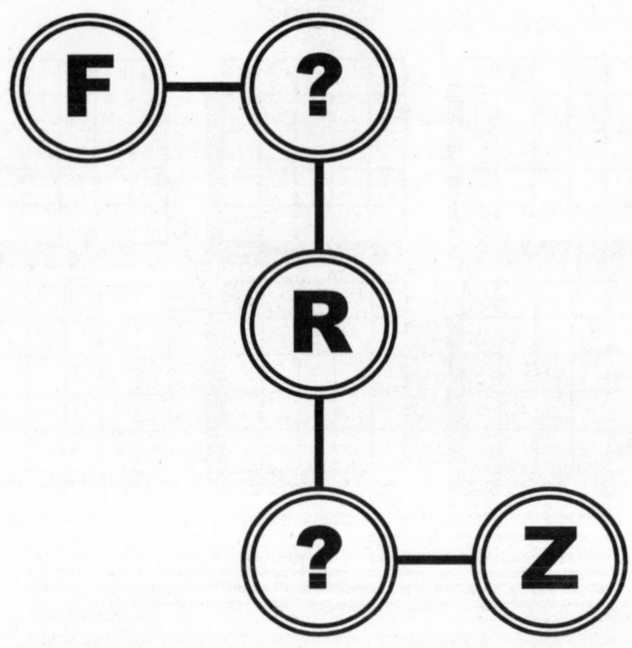

25

Is Leonardo DiCaprio associated with London, Portsmouth, Bristol or Southampton?

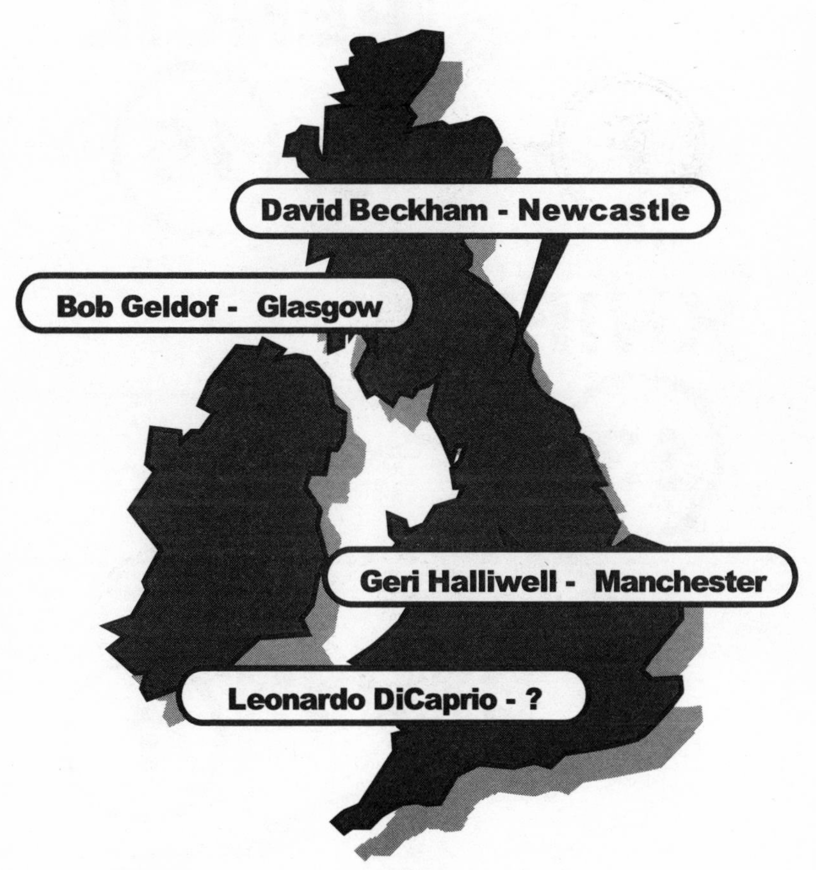

26

What number should accompany the brush?

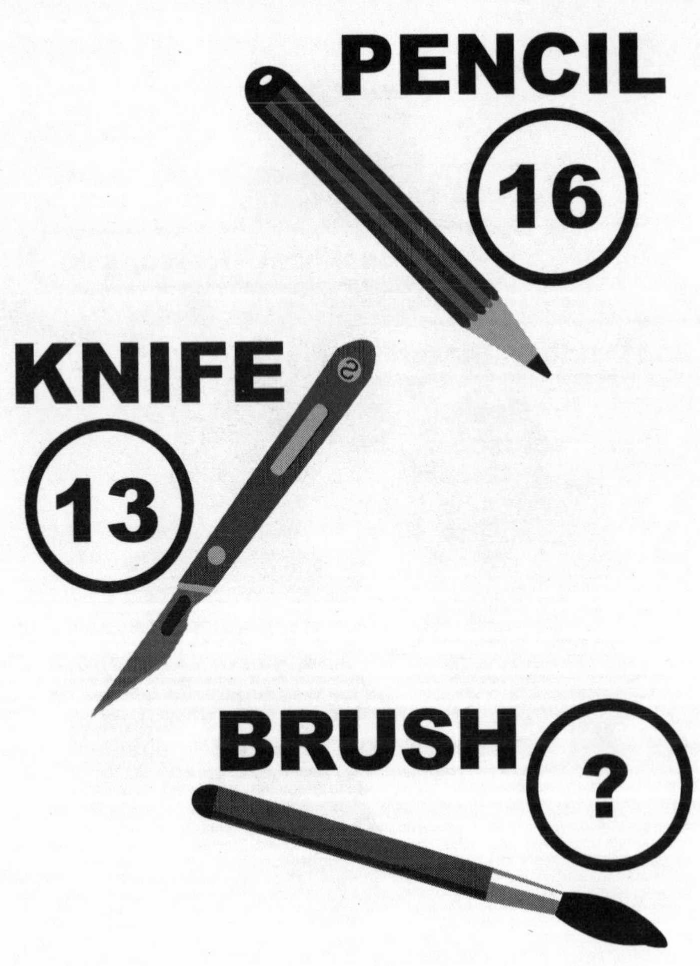

27

Is Dolly Parton associated with Dallas or Washington?

28

Can you decode this popular holiday destination?

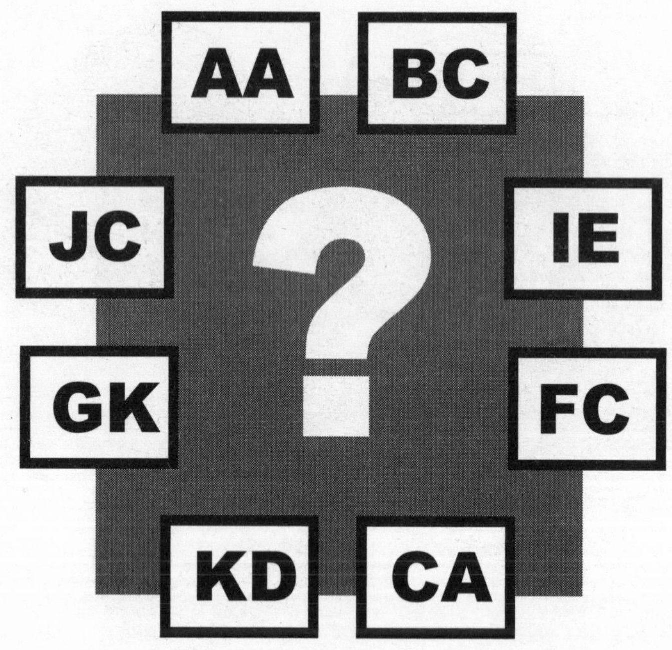

29

Which letter is the odd one out?

30

Which code number will connect up these two computers?

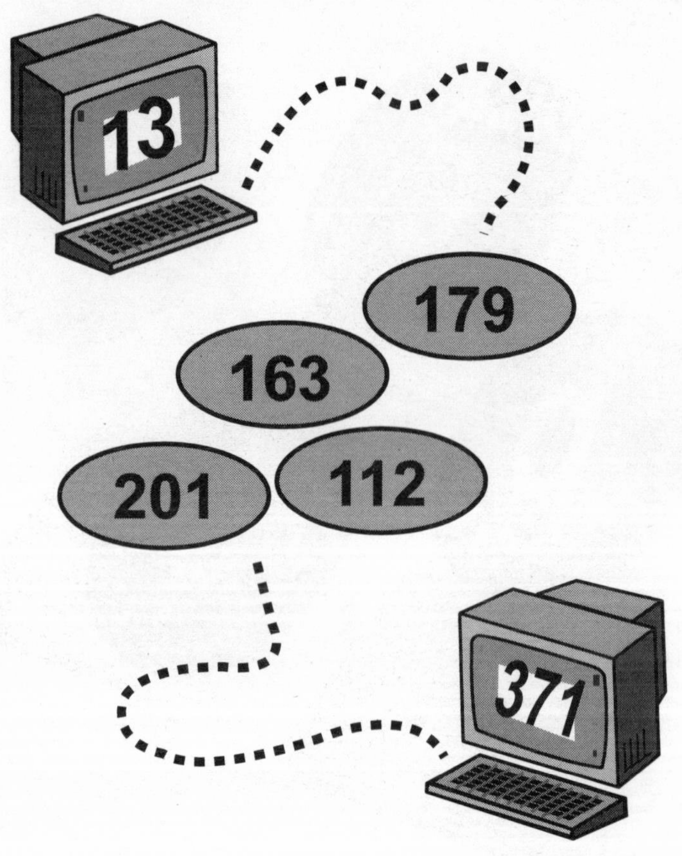

31

The novels below have sold these numbers of copies in the UK during the past five years.

How many copies of *Cider with Rosie* have been sold?

32

Which piece of cable will connect up the lightbulb?

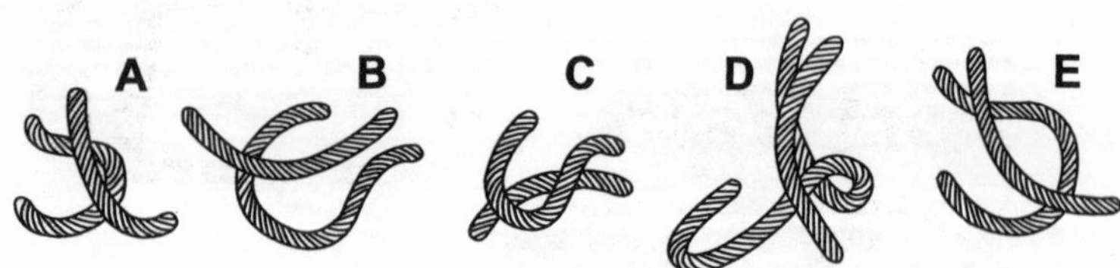

33

On each football shirt are the number of goals each team has scored this month.

How many has Liverpool scored?

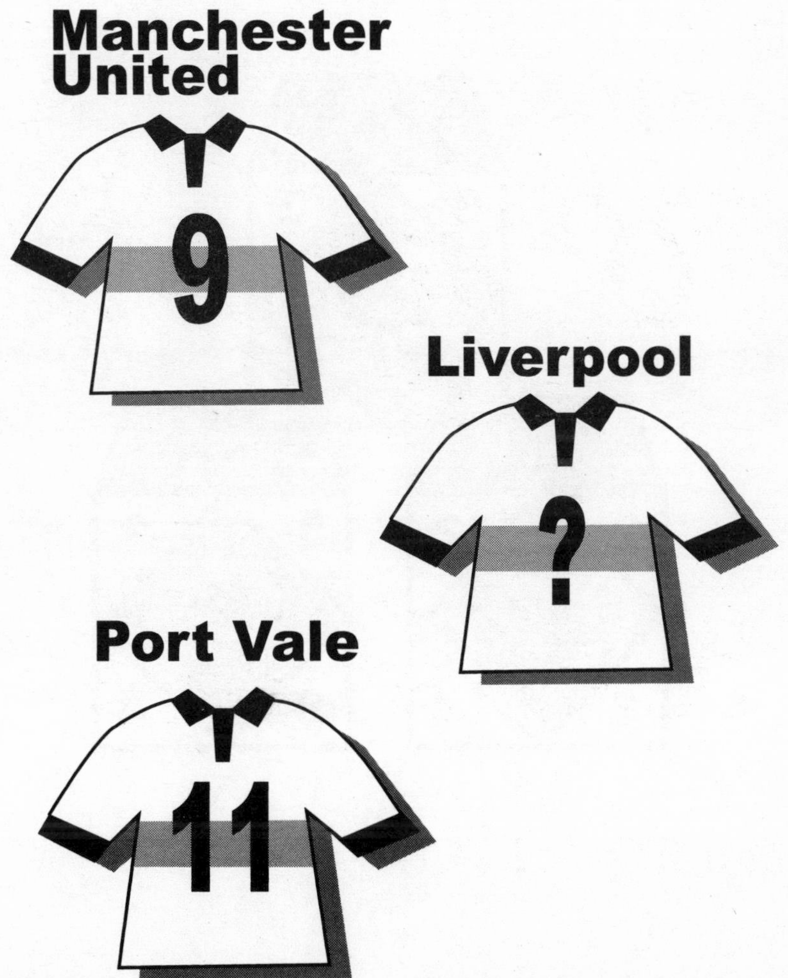

34

What number should you put in box C?

Recently, a survey was carried out to discover what people did last New Year's Eve.

How many of them stayed in?

36

What is the score on target C?

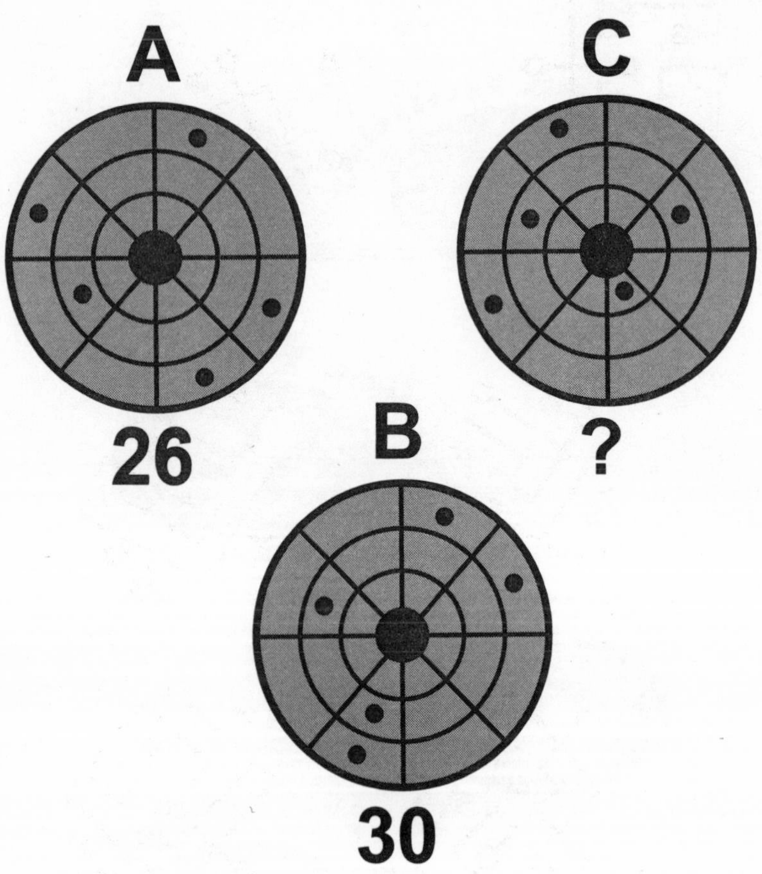

37

Which shape is not a mirror image of the one below?

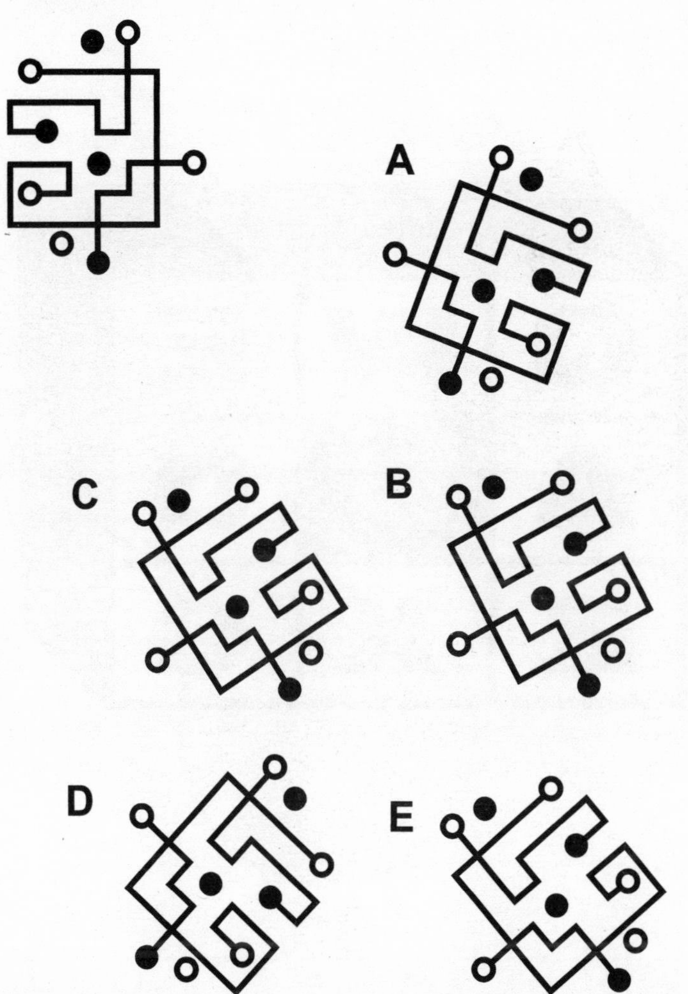

38

Which letter is missing?

39

Which construction is the odd one out?

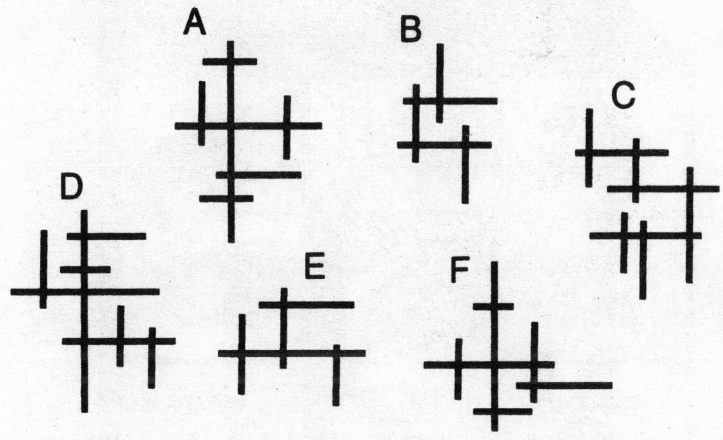

40

Does the A4515 go to Nantwich, Winterley or Oakhanger?

41

Which two tiles don't match the others?

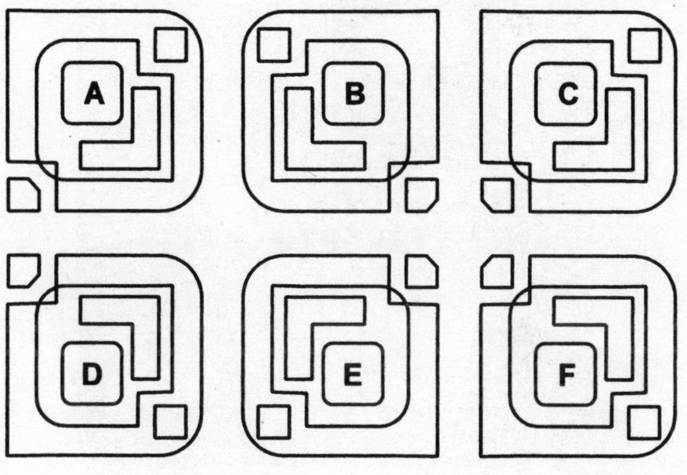

42

What are the last four digits in Mike Scott's passport number?

BILL STONE
No: 11243929

MIKE SCOTT
No: 2216????

JOHN ADAMS
No: 25220514

43

At what times do the trains to Rugby and Stafford leave?

44

You have received this coded message.

What does it say?

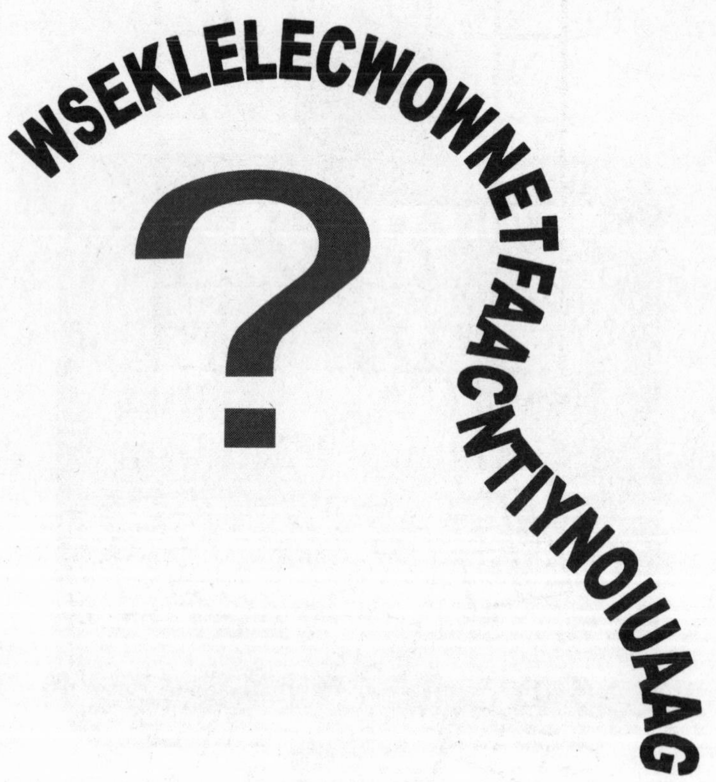

Put in the correct piece.

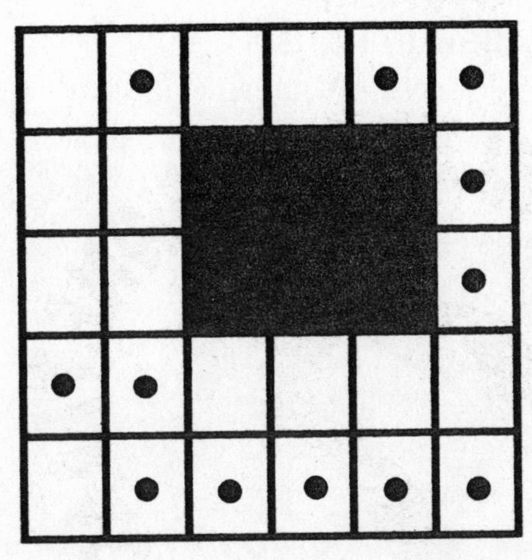

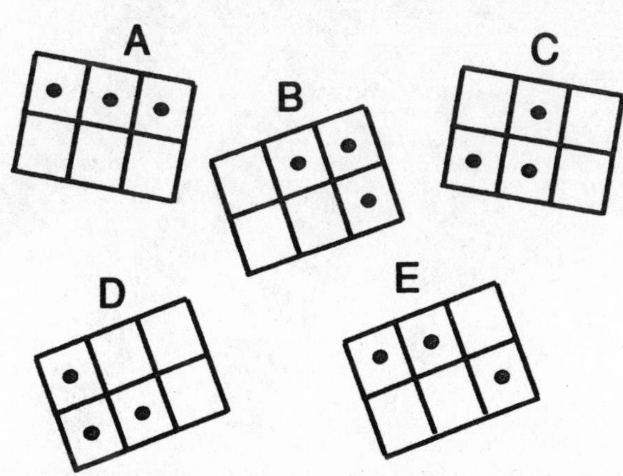

46

110 people flew from Heathrow to Amsterdam, 40 flew to Manchester, and 160 to Brussels.

How many flew to Paris?

Find the missing number.

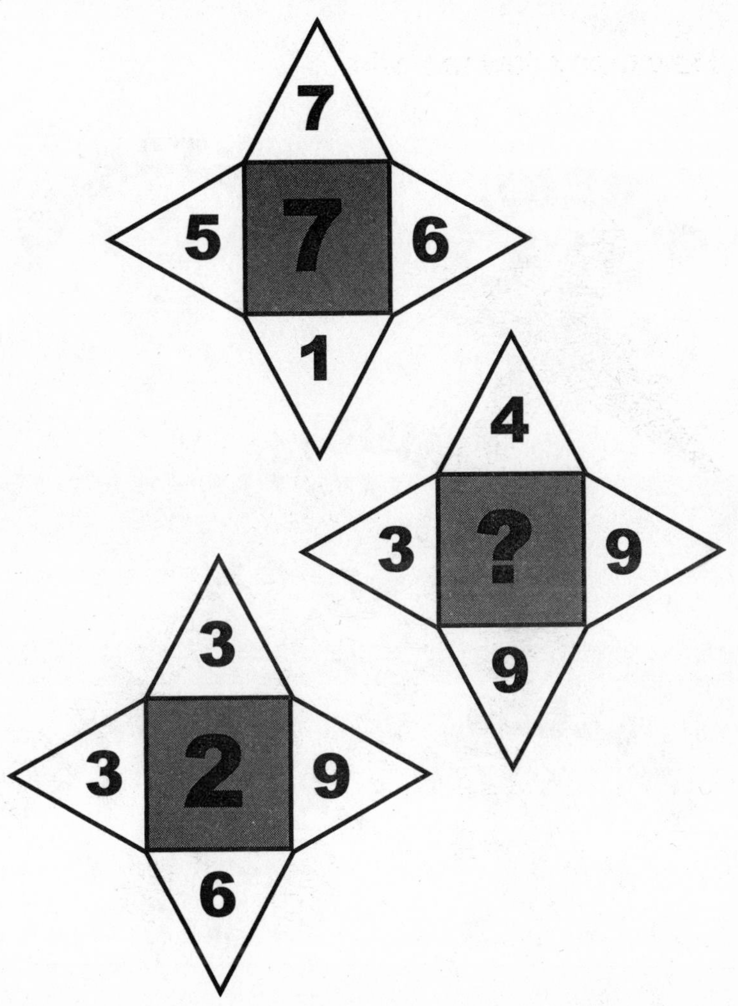

Unravel these winter sun holiday destinations and then decide which one doesn't belong with the others.

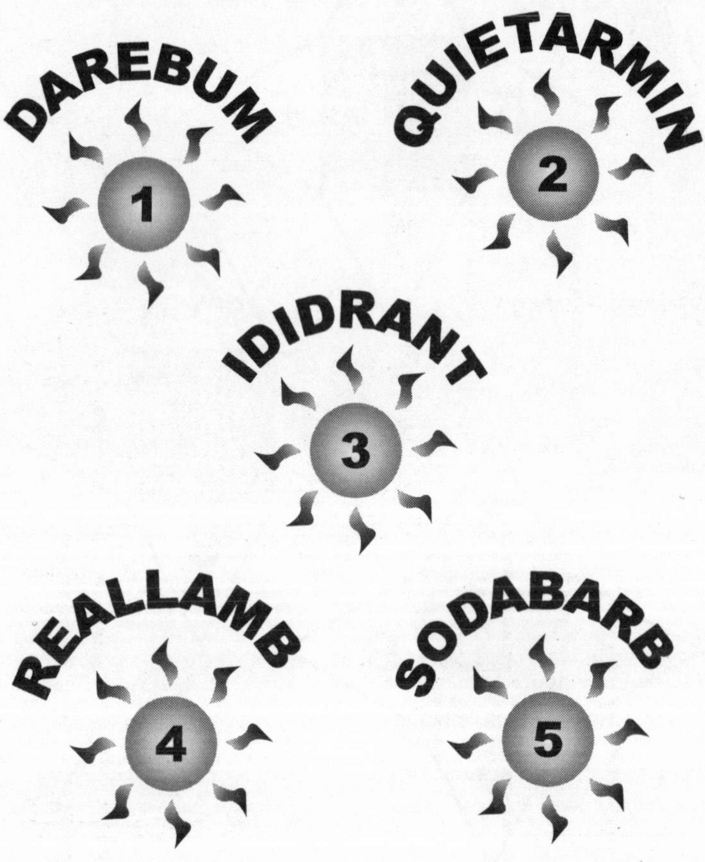

49

Which of the four pieces below will connect up this circuit?

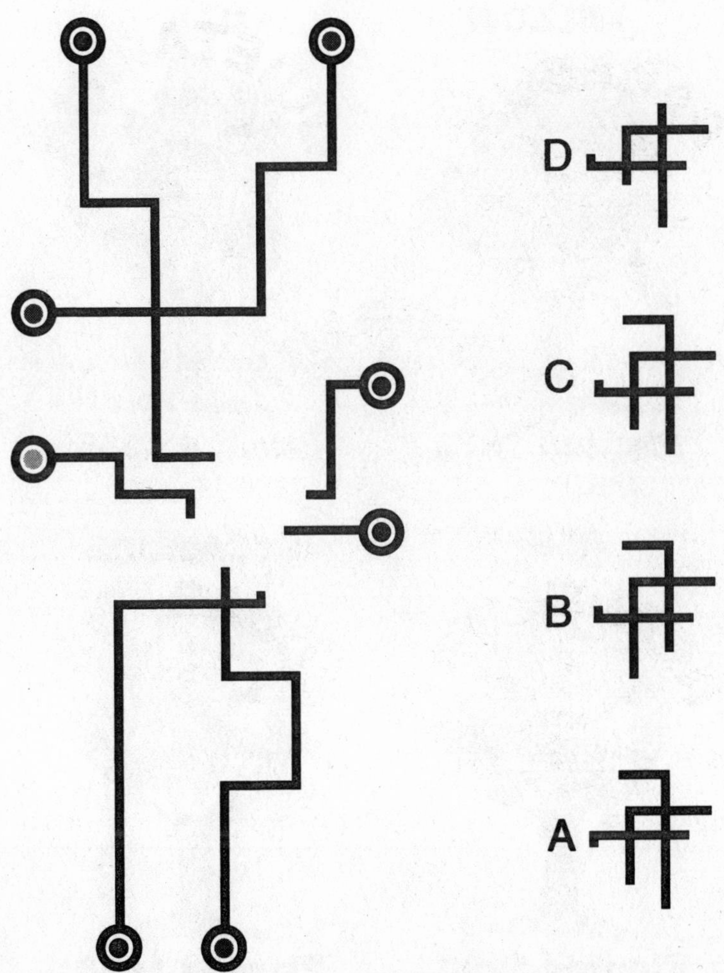

Each of these trees has reached a certain height.

How tall is the sycamore tree?

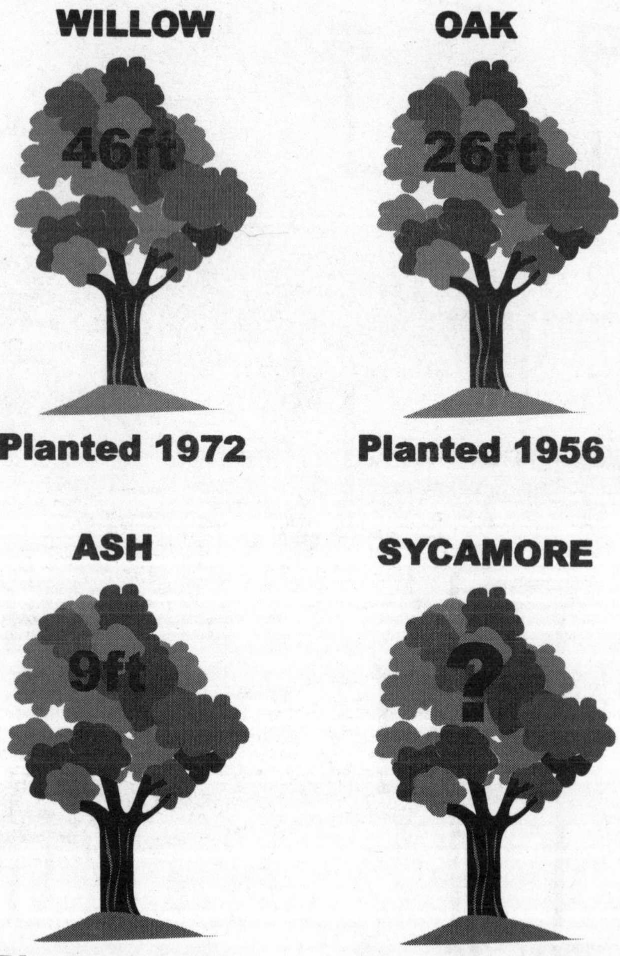

51

Which of these classic number plates is the odd one out?

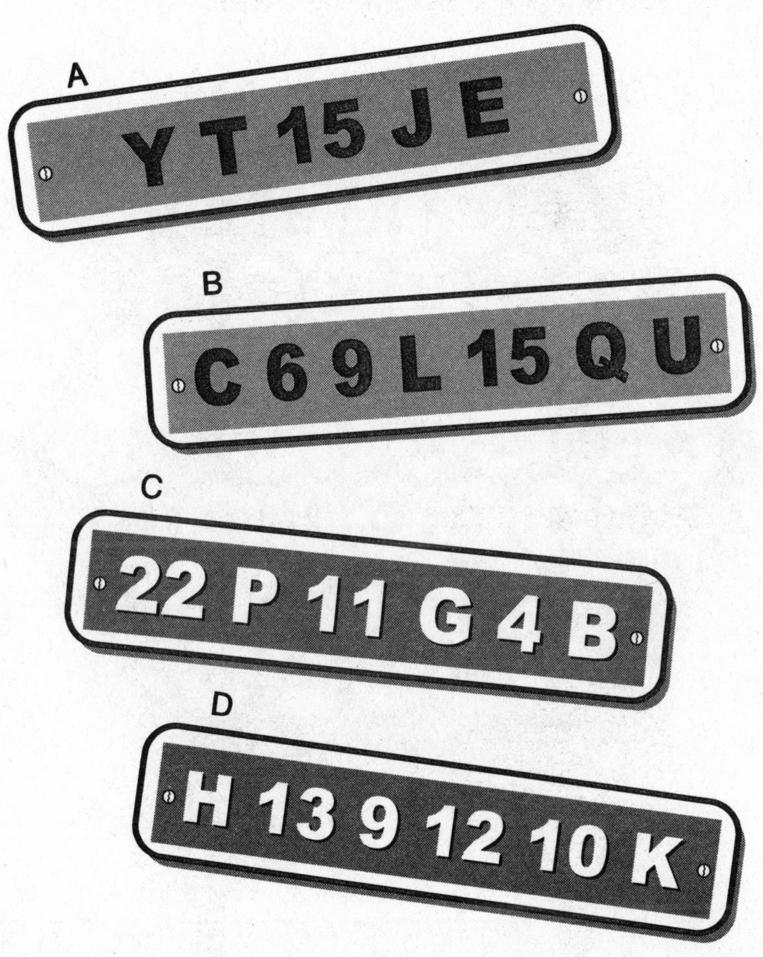

52

Move from circle to circle to find the name of a well-known comic actor and television presenter.

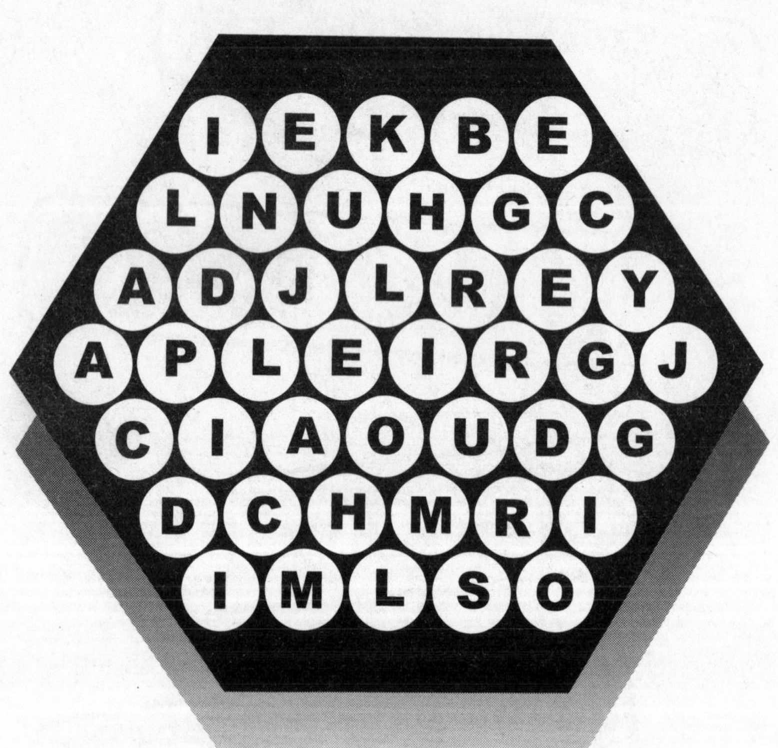

53

What is the last number in this sequence?

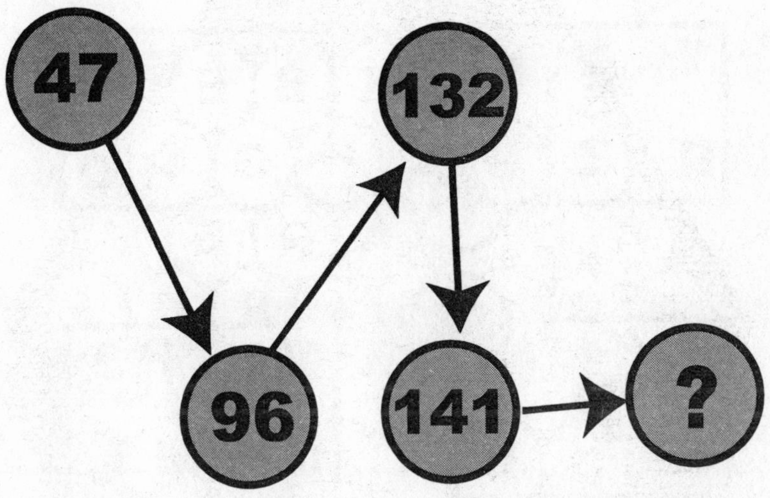

54

Which number should appear in the bottom right circle?

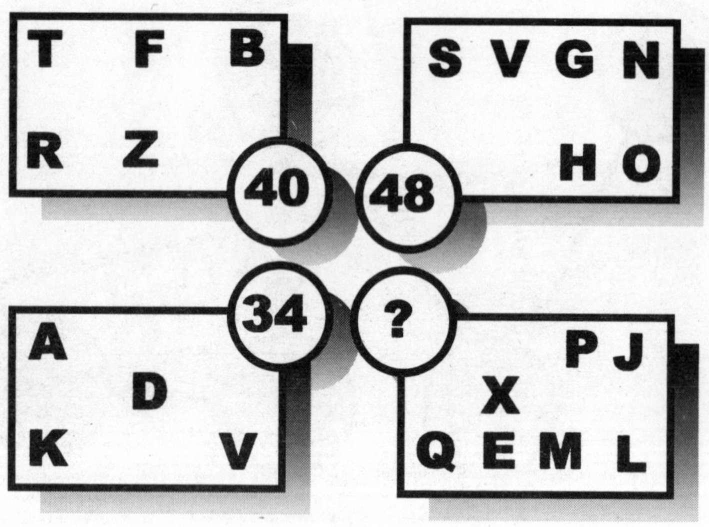

Fill in the missing numbers.

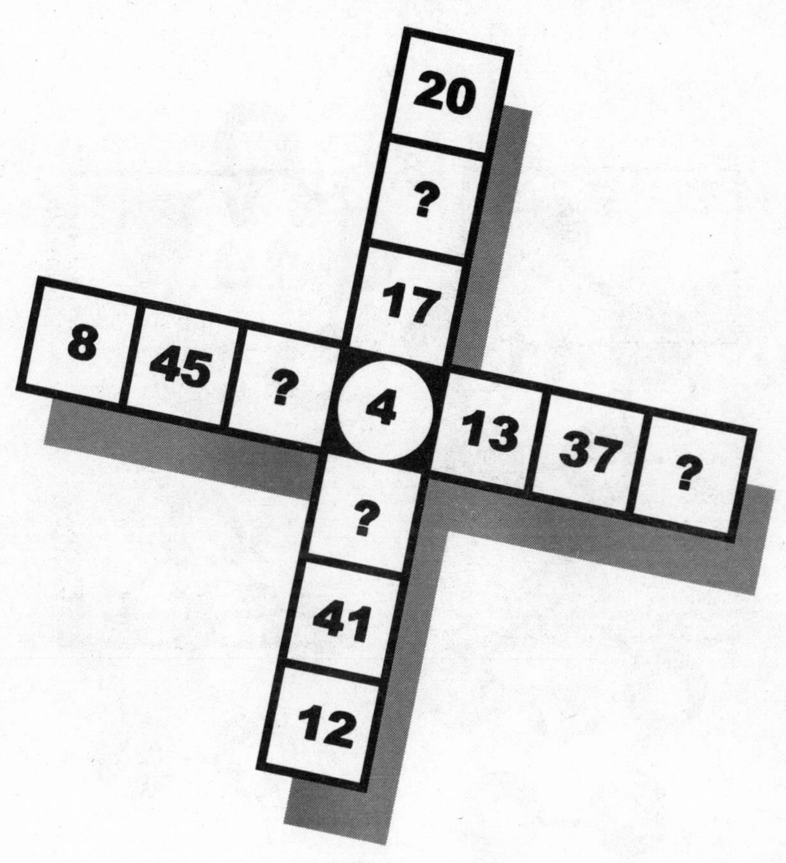

56

What is the value of the question mark?

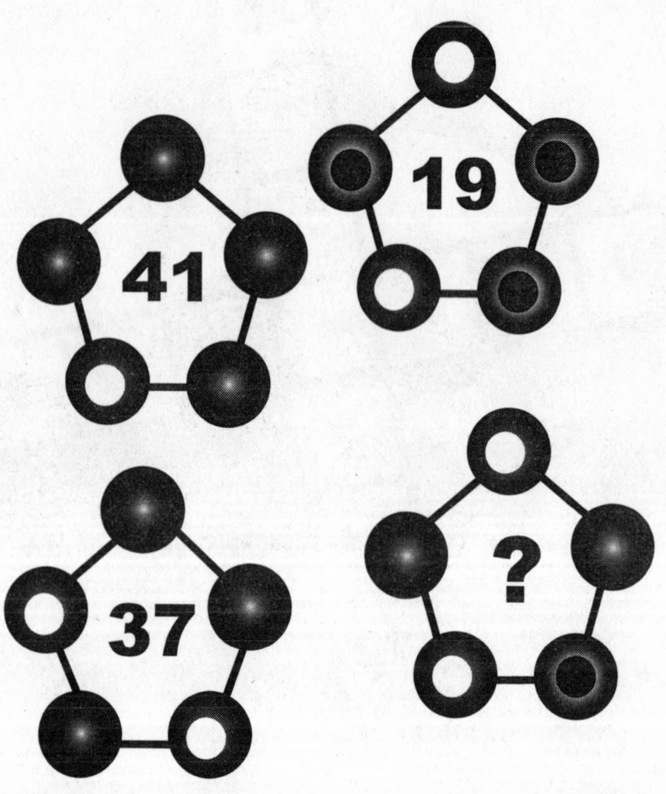

57

What are the missing letters?

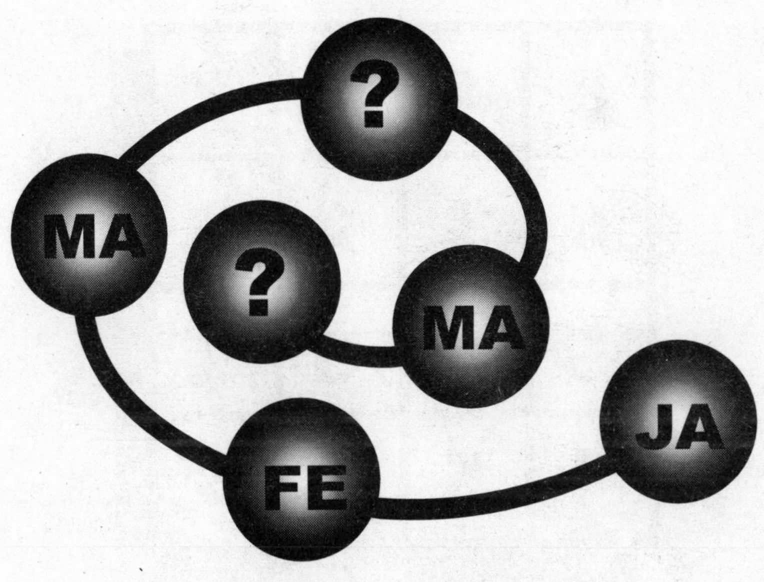

58

Which two numbers are missing from this grid?

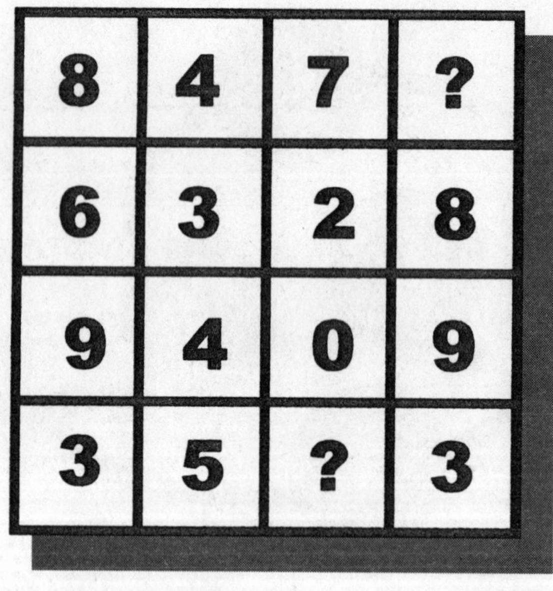

59

Find the missing two numbers to open the safe.

EMERALD

DIAMOND

SAPPHIRE

TOPAZ

RUBY

60

Crack the code to discover the word.

61

In the grid below find Norwich, Leeds, Derby, York and Stoke. The remaining letters spell out another English town. What is it?

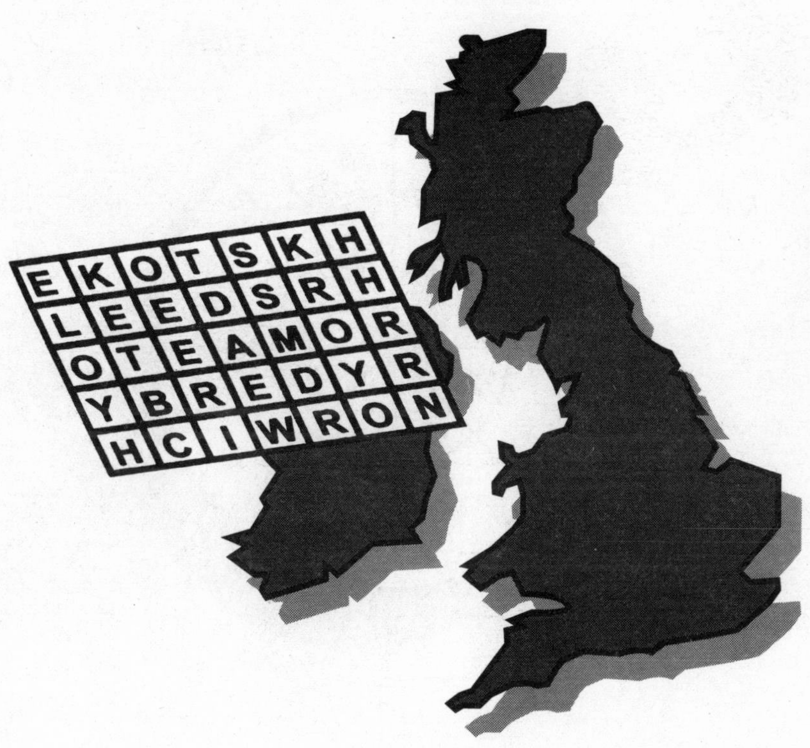

62

Find the two numbers missing from the centre of this wheel.

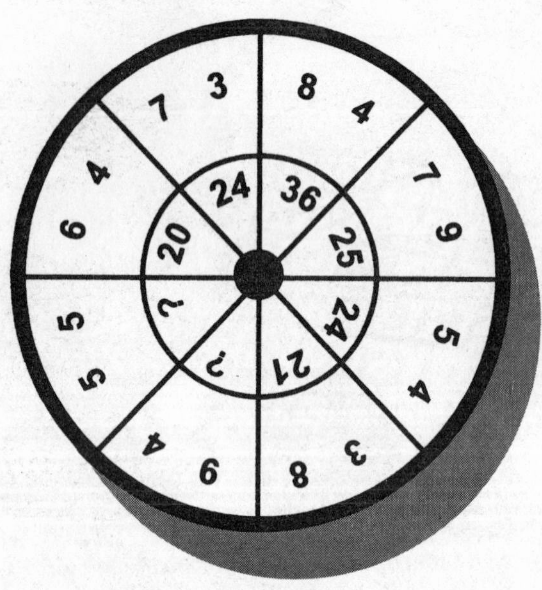

63

Which person doesn't belong in this group?

64

What odds are currently given on Lea Tortuga?

65

What is the missing number?

66

Here is a map showing the number of stations on the route to various destinations.

How many are on the Euston to Poole route?

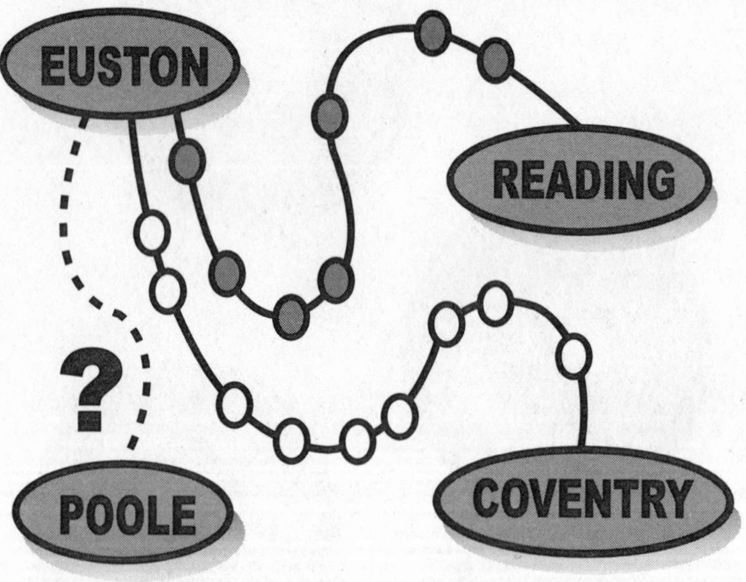

Erica's favourite meal is beef steak, her best friend is called Carol, her hobby is swimming and she likes to travel by bicycle.

Does she like to watch chat shows or documentaries on television?

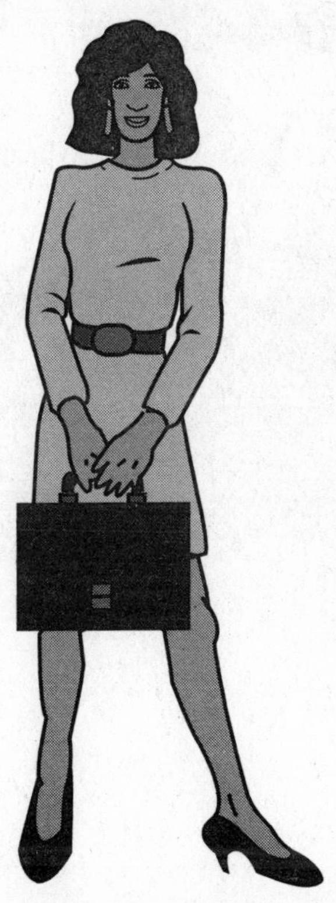

68

You need to call Michael Maclean Taxis, but what is the last digit in his phone number?

Mixed together below are five European countries each with their unit of currency.

Unravel them all to find the odd one out.

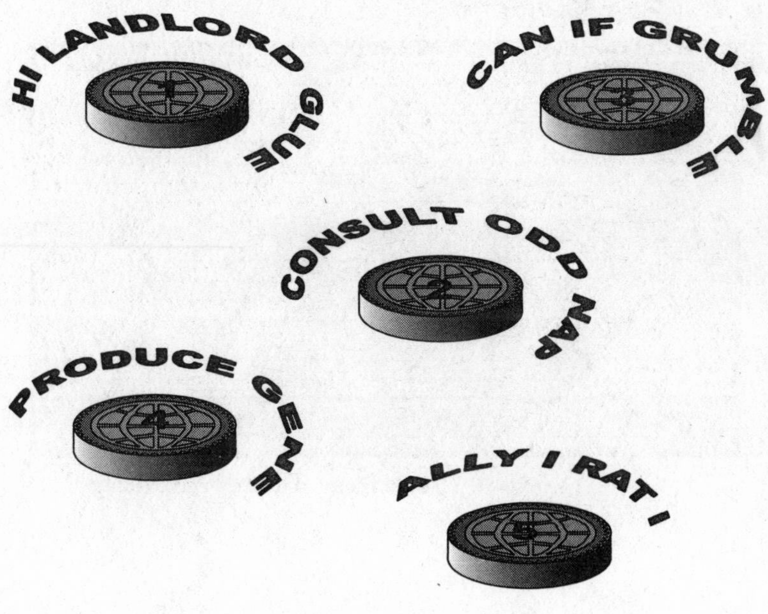

This chart shows the average monthly rainfall over a five-month period.

What was it in November?

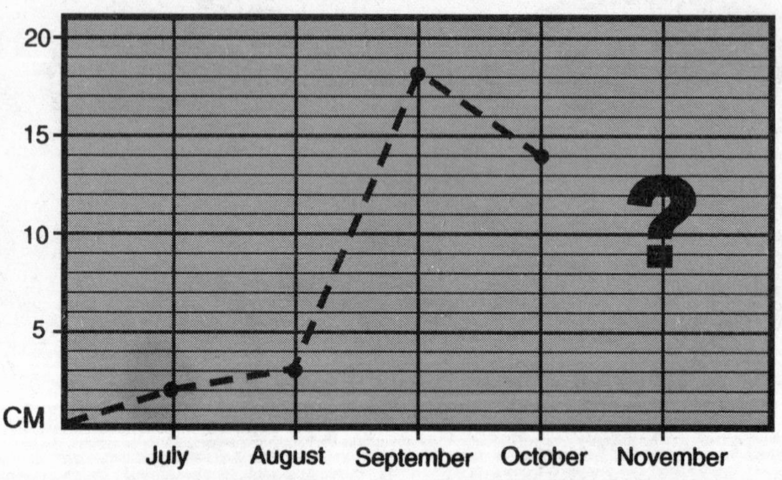

71

Which shape does not belong with the others?

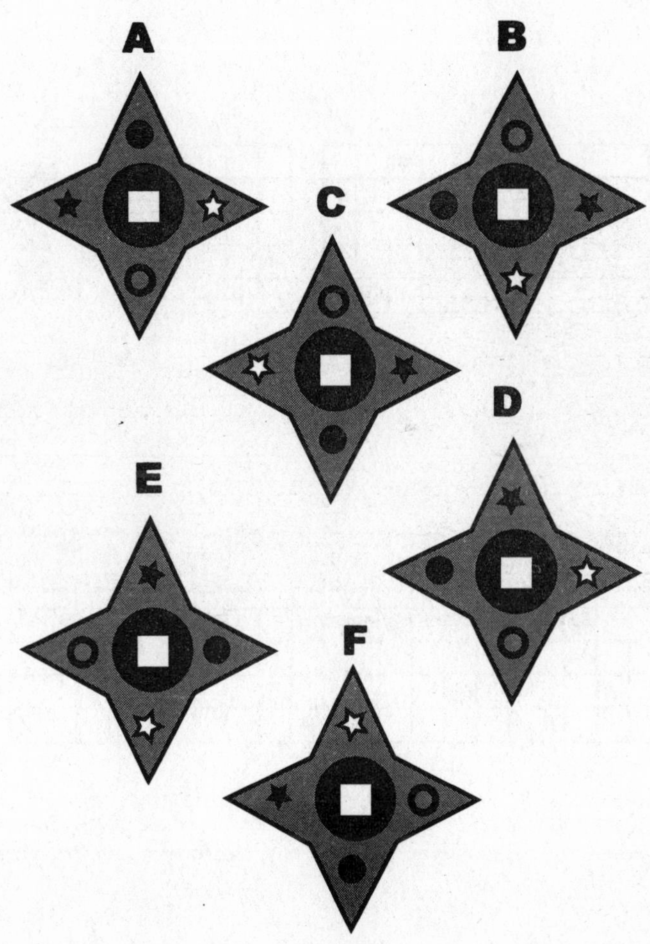

72

Which comes next in this sequence?

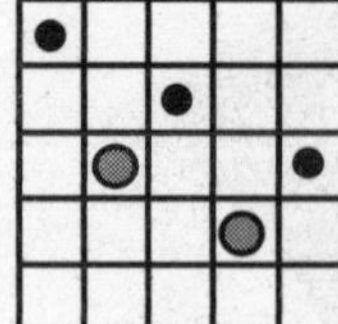
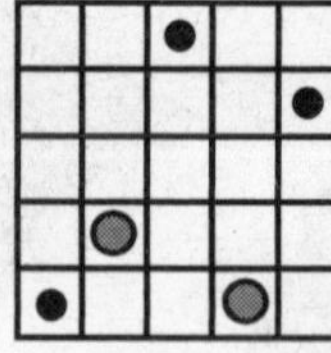
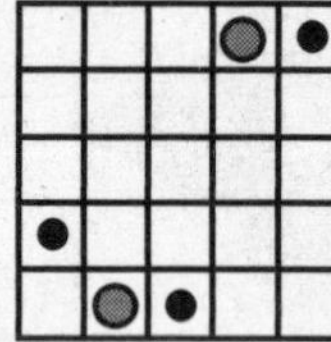

A

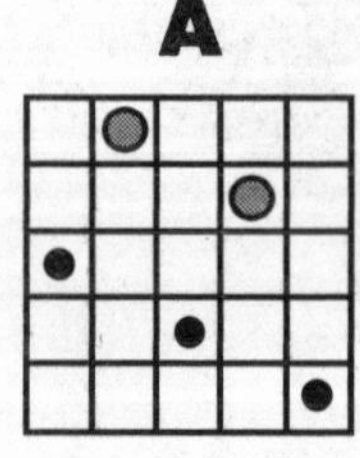

B

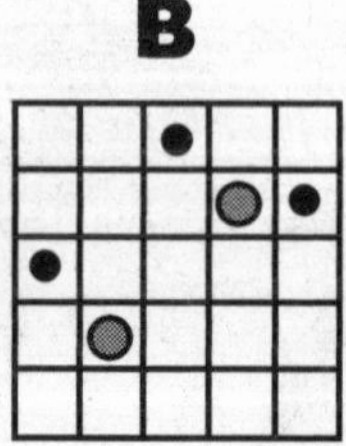

C

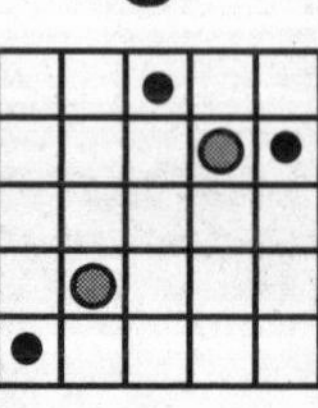

D

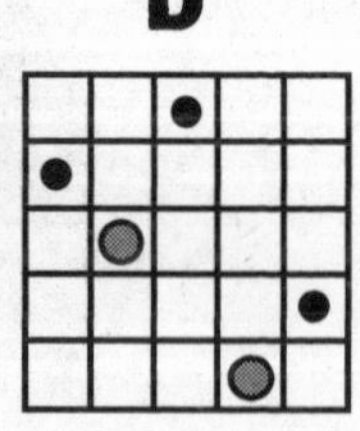

73

Crack this code to discover the word.

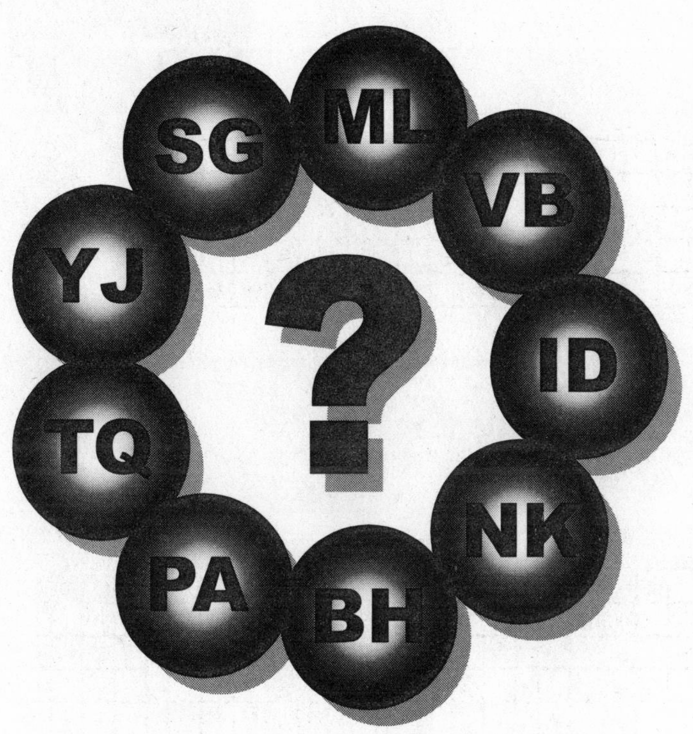

74

Which is the only piece that completes the square?

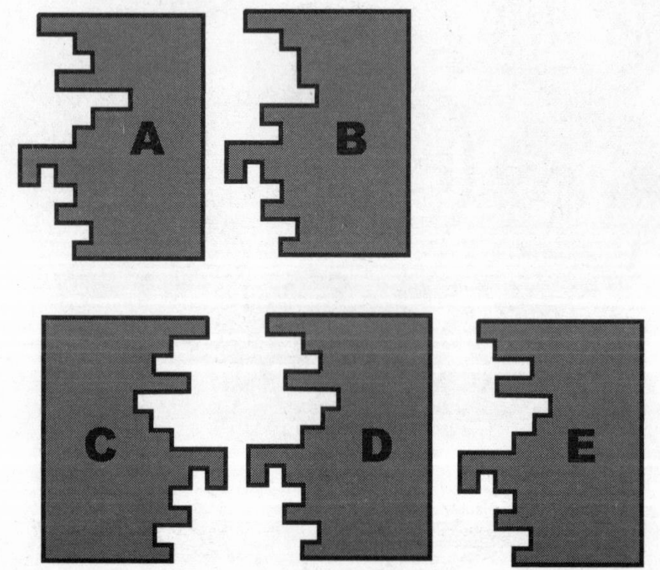

75

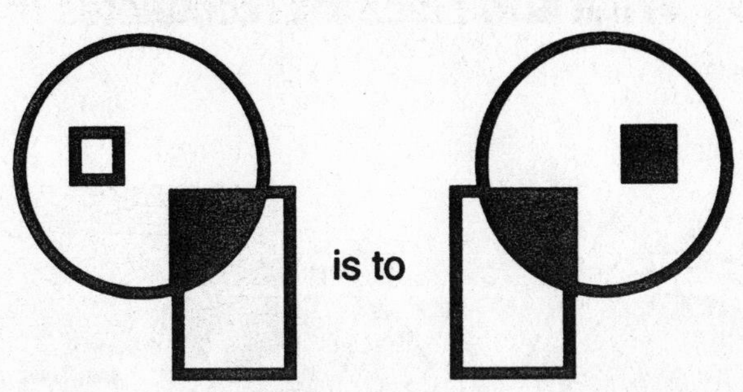

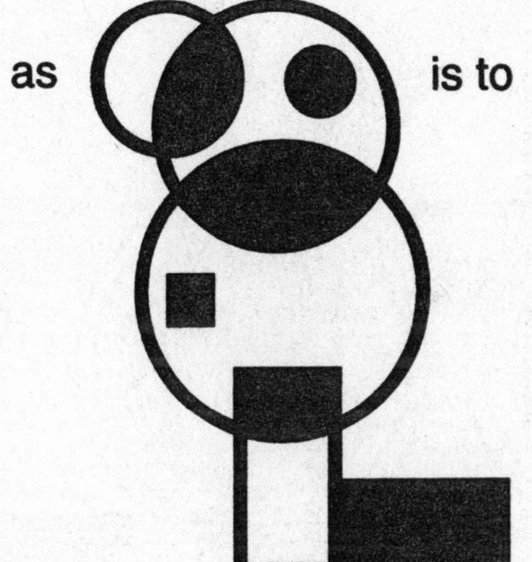

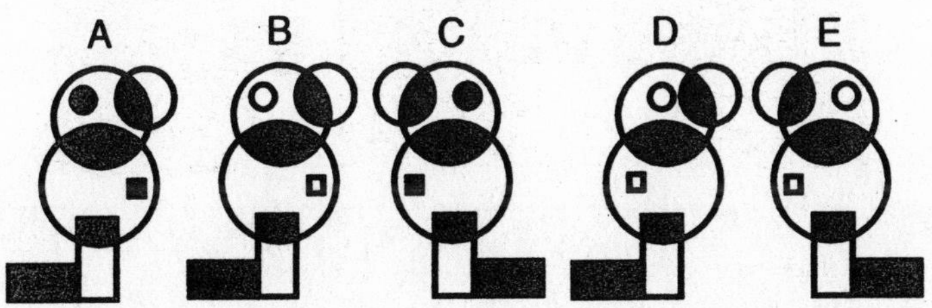

76

What is the missing number?

77

Can you work out David's telephone number from his business card?

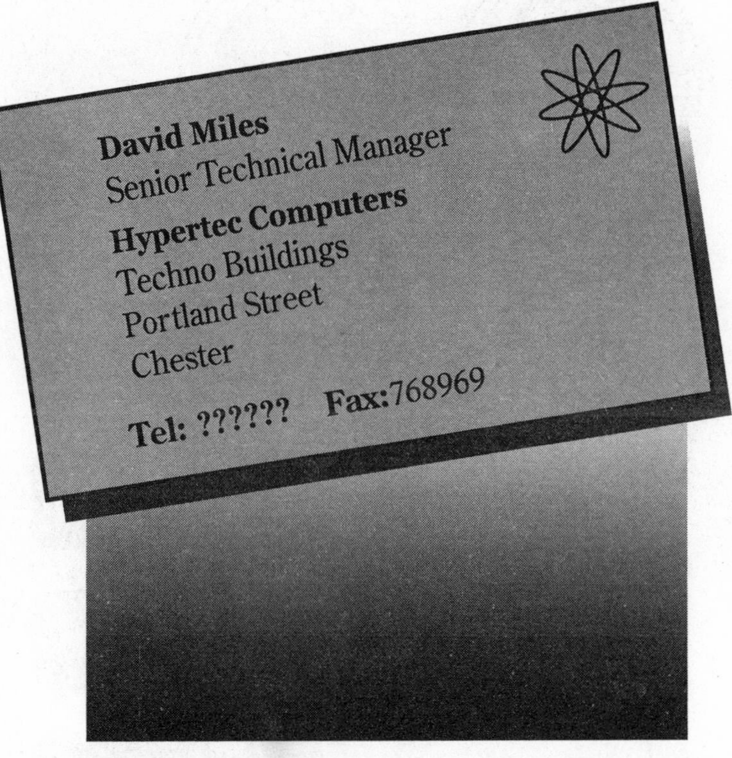

Take the vowels from the circle and add them to the rectangles to make four words. Then decide which word is the odd one out.

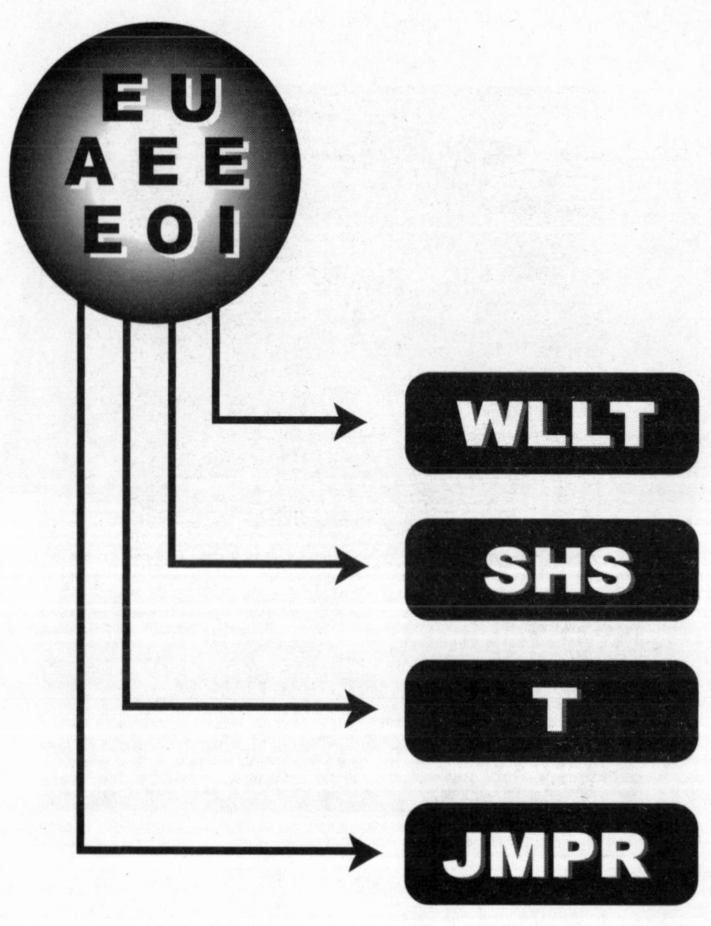

79

What are the values of each of the shapes?

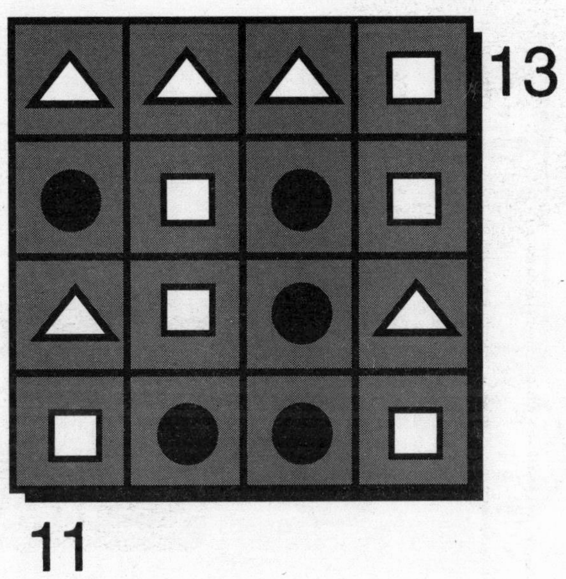

80

Which number should you put in the fourth column?

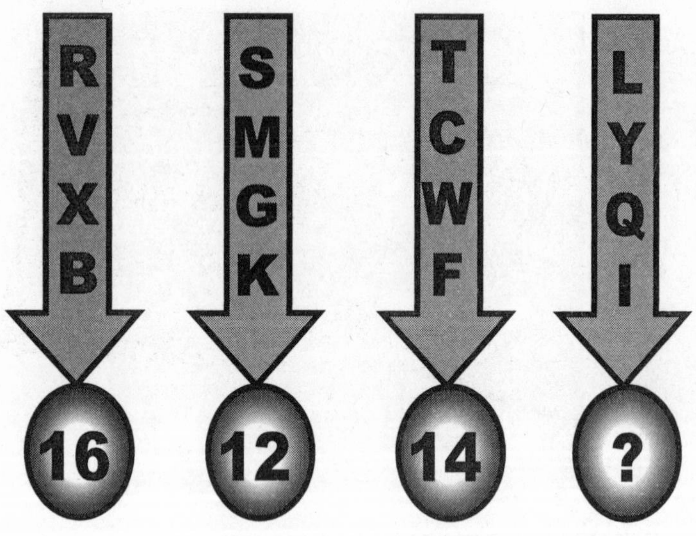

81

What does this coded message say?

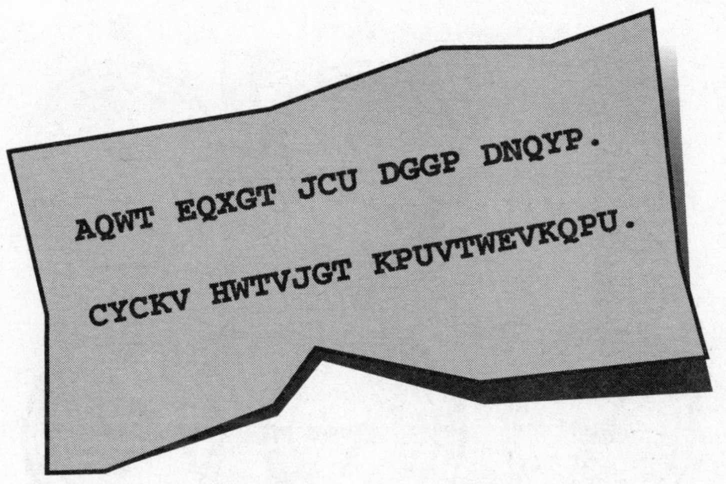

82

What time should it be on clock E?

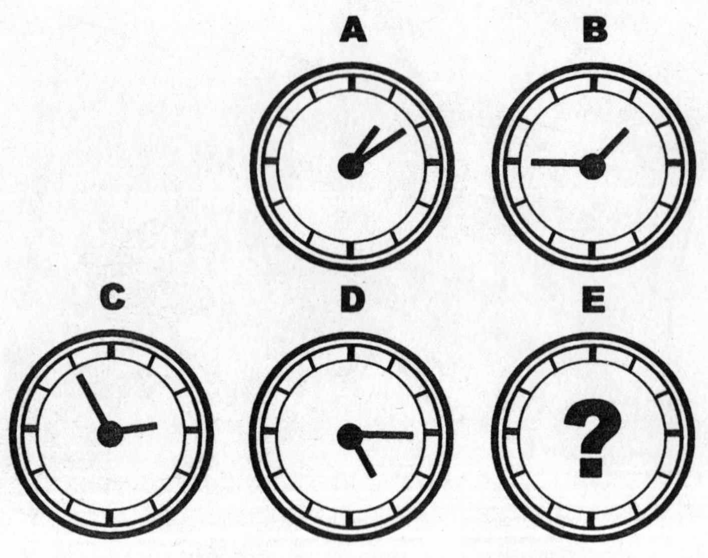

83

Work out the missing number.

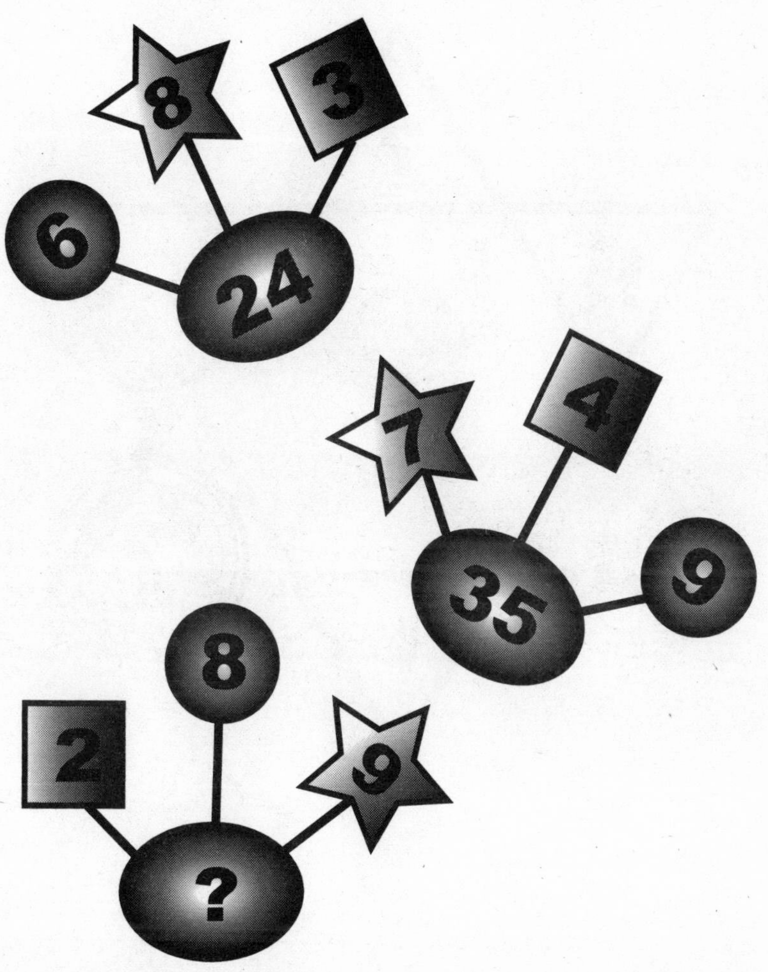

84

Find the missing letter.

85

Where has your friend gone on holiday?

86

Which two letters are missing?

Which terminal should you choose to connect up this cable?

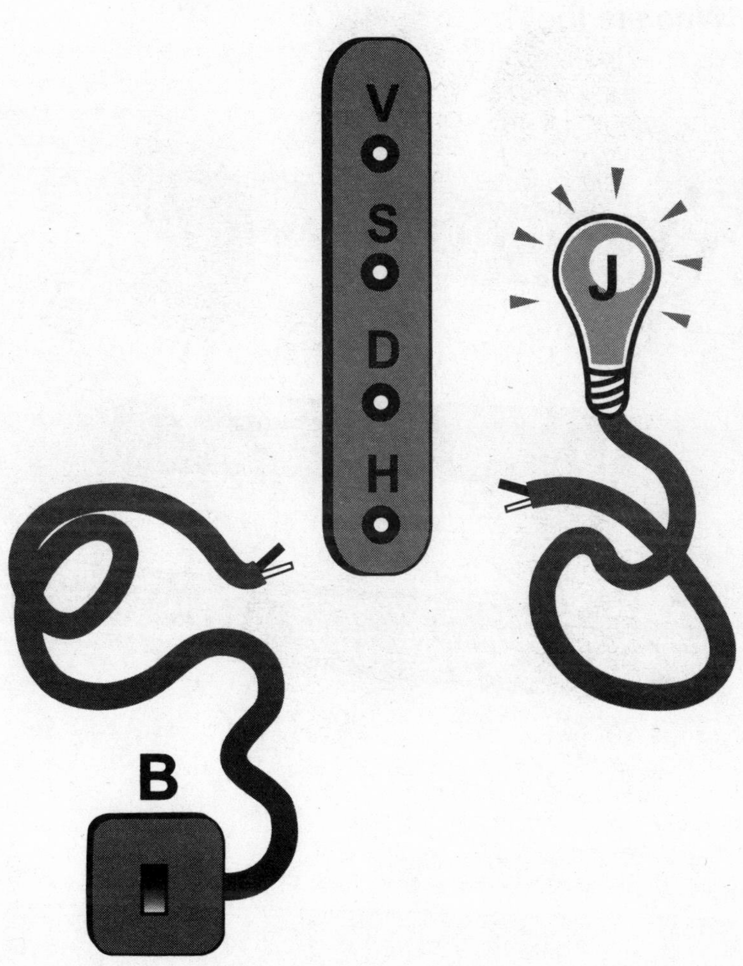

The names of three famous historical figures are written here in code.

Who are they?

A

B

C

89

Can you find the missing piece of this barcode?

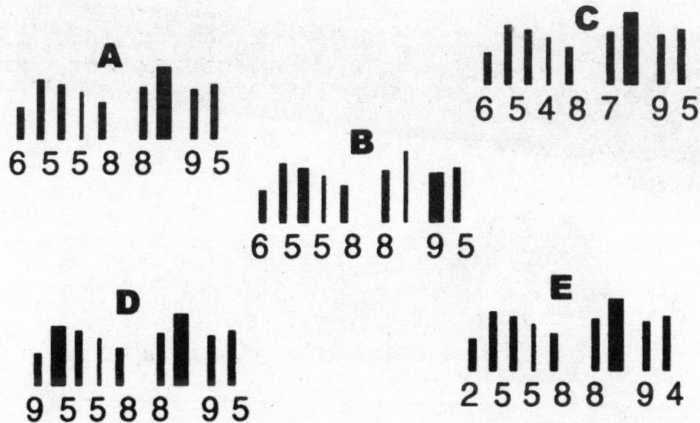

90

Find the two missing numbers.

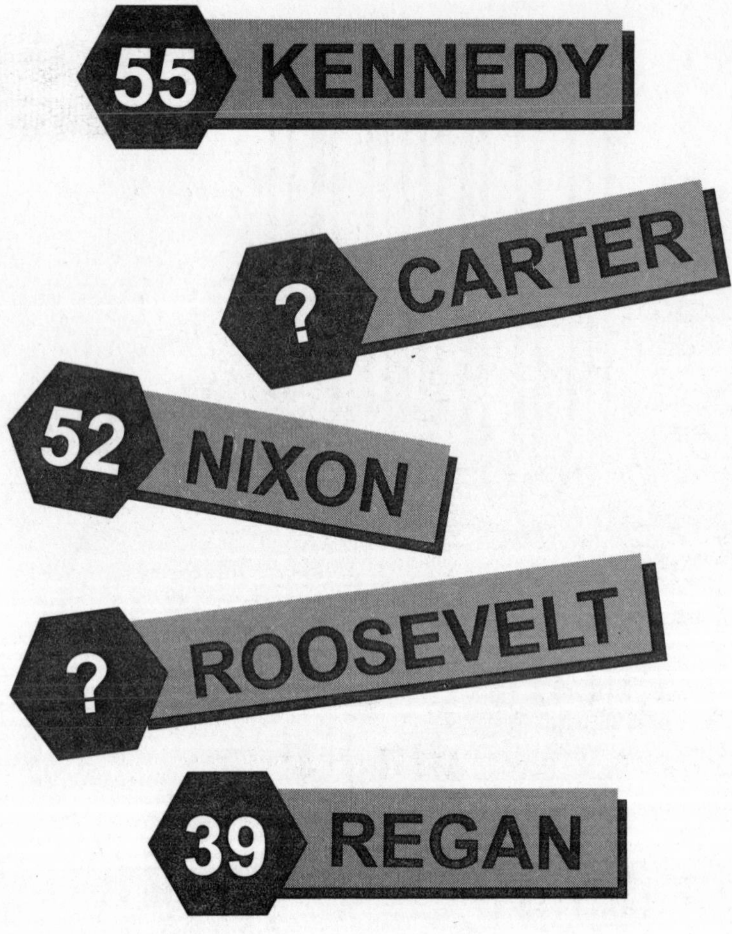

91

Which number is missing from this bingo card?

Which two numbers should replace the question marks?

93

Which symbol is a mirror image of the one below?

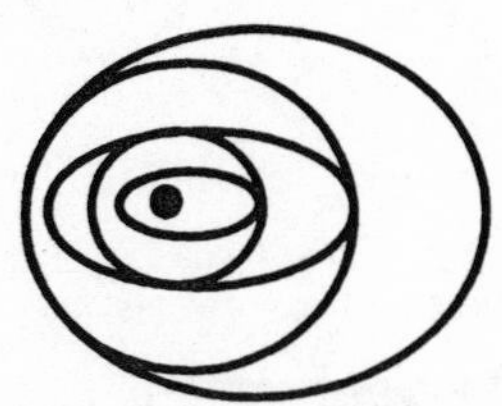

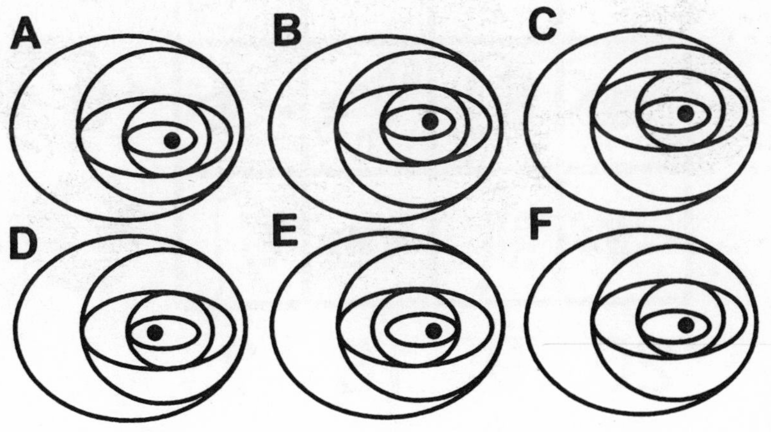

Can you find the two missing numbers?

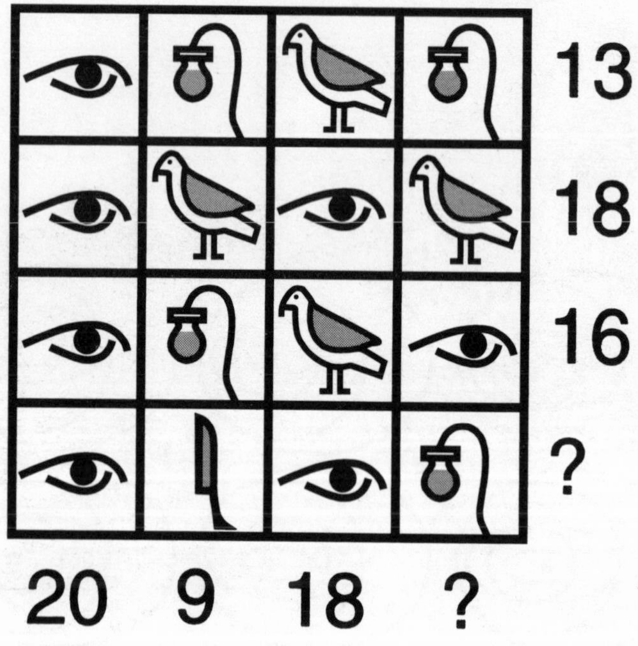

95

Recently, five food retailers set up internet sites.

Which is the odd one out?

96

Move from square to square, including diagonally, to find the name of a popular TV quiz show.

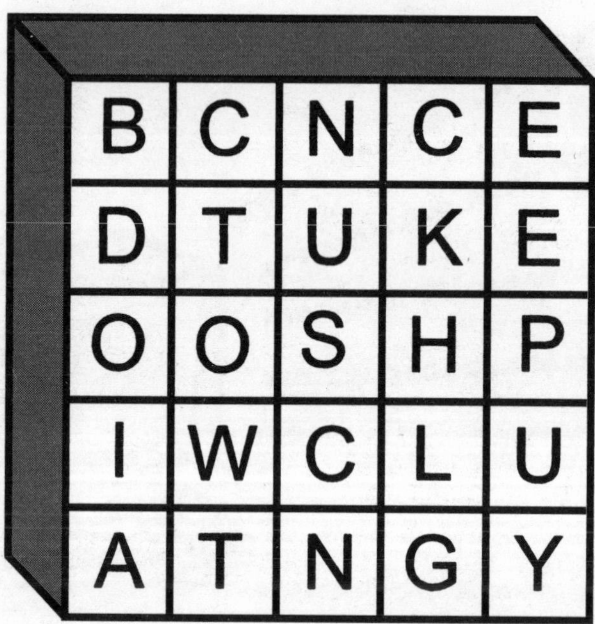

97

If ♦□■⊠ ♌●♋♓❒ is TONY BLAIR, then who are these other politicians?

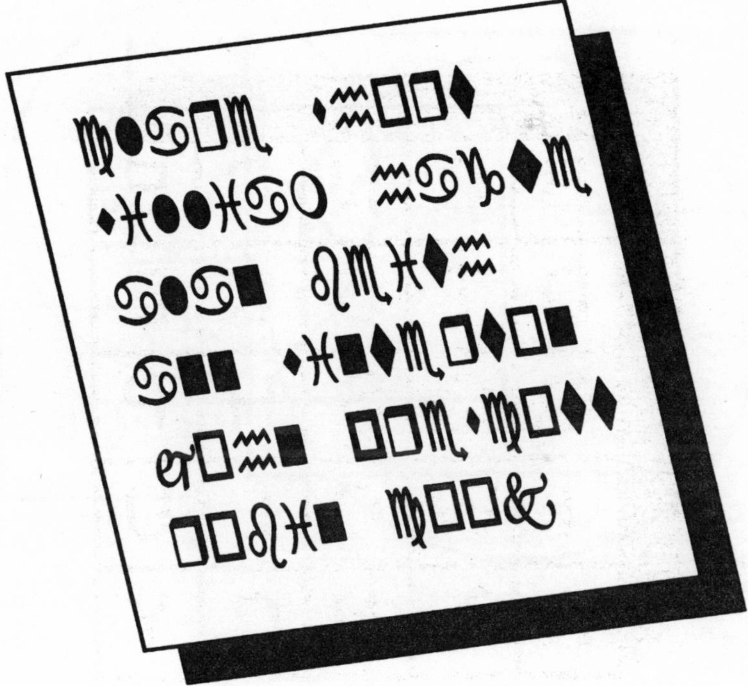

98

What are the two missing numbers?

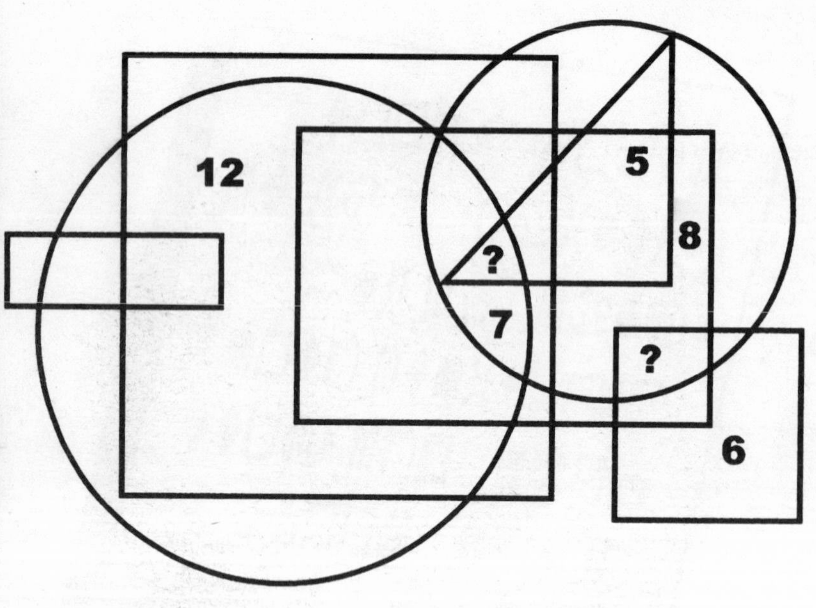

99

How many 'click stops' right or left must you turn the outer dial so that all the sections add up to seven?

100

Can you work out the name of the well-known TV programme from the letters below?

Solutions

1 'People who live in glass houses shouldn't throw stones.'

2 Good Friday.

3 E. All of the others contain eight straight lines while this one contains seven.

4 Tony Blair.

5 £58. Starting with the first letter, take the alphanumeric value of every other letter in the word and add them together.

6 D. The circle rotates 90 degrees clockwise each time, with the big circle and two smaller ones swapping from black to white.

7 689.

8 Three years. In each case, remove any letter from the family name and multiply the number of remaining letters by the house number. Then take the answer down to it's lowest form, e.g., O'Neil=4, 4 x 3=12, 1+2=3

9

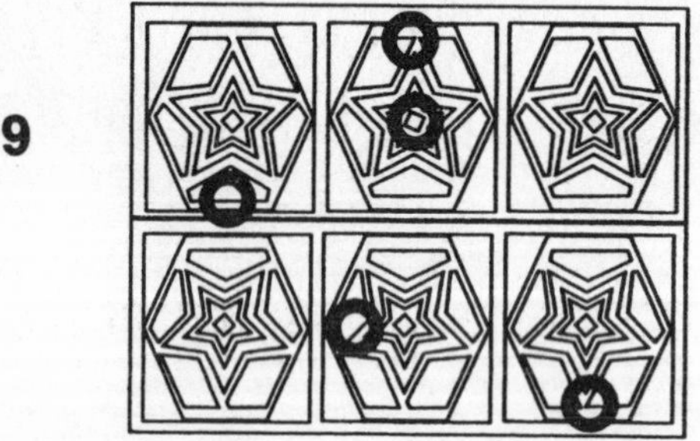

10 St Emilion. The alphanumeric value of each letter of 'Jane Smith' gives the position of each letter hidden in the code. (E.g., J is the 10th letter of the alphabet and the 10th letter of the code is S, so the first letter of her favourite wine is S.)

11 A Rover. All of Ian's choices contain two vowels.

12 E. The shapes are hands on a clock which move on by an hour and a quarter each time. E is a quarter to seven.

13 Second row V, third row K. The alphanumeric values of each row add up to 46.

14 B. All the other shapes are symmetrical.

15 20. Each is the same as the alphanumeric value of the last letter of the word.

16 D. A is the same as F, B is the same as G and C is the same as E.

17 C. Each letter is the next but one following each vowel.

18 Berlin 18.12 and Istanbul 01.14. The alphanumeric values of the two middle letters of each destination.

19 3. The number of bookings is really the number of letters from the first letter of the day, to the end of the alphabet.

20 The Exorcist. The answer to each sum is the alphanumeric position of each letter in the film title.

21

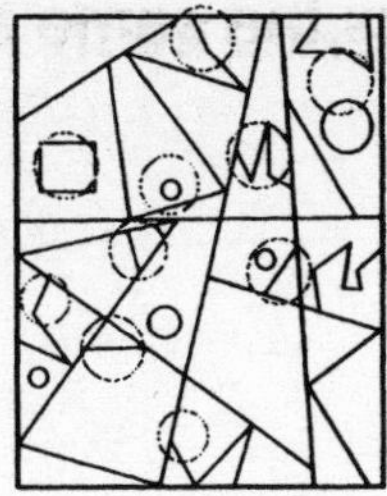

22 F.

23 The top right corner. Its first move was 1 square anti-clockwise around the outside of the square, then 2, then 4, then 8, and finally 16.

24 L and V. The alphanumeric values of the five vowels are reversed so that O becomes L and E becomes V.

25 Portsmouth. The first letter of the place follows alphabetically from the last letter of the person's name.

26 14. Each vowel is worth 2 and each consonant is worth 3.

27 Washington. Each person's name has the same number of vowels as the place name.

28 Benidorm. Add together the alphanumeric values of each two letters to give the alphanumeric value of each letter in the name.

29 S. This is the only letter not to contain an enclosed space.

30 179. This number is halfway between 13 and 371.

31 42,000. Multiply the number of letters in the book title by the number of words in the book title, then multiply by 1,000.

32 E.

33 0. Take the alphanumerical value of the last letter of the name from the first one.

34 20. In each box, multiply the diagonal numbers, then add them together and place the total in the next box (2x4=8, 2x6=12, 8+12=20).

35 11. The number of letters in the phrase added to the number of vowels contained in it.

36 59.

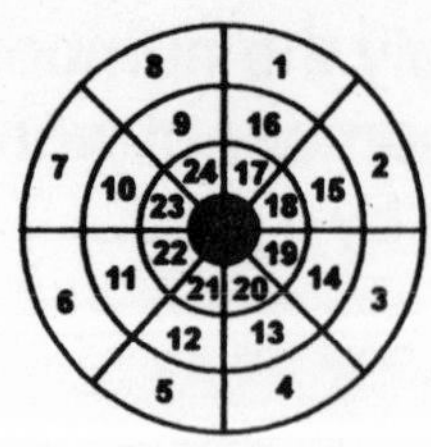

37 E.

38 S. These letters are from the start of a standard 'QWERTY' keyboard:
QWERTYUIOP
ASDFGHJKL
ZXCVBNM

39 D. This is the only one with an equal number of horizontal and vertical lines.

40 Oakhanger. The road number is A if an odd number of letters and B if an even number. Then the rest is made up of firstly the number of vowels, then the number of consonants, and finally the alphanumeric value of the first letter.

41 A and D.

42 2235. The alphanumeric values of the first two letters are added together then the next two and so on. The final letter in the name is ignored.

43 Both leave at 17.00 hrs. Take the alphanumeric value of the first letter of the place then take away the number of vowels in the place.

44 'We'll contact you again in a few weeks.' Starting with the letter W, read every other letter to the end and back again.

45 B. One space is followed by one dot, two spaces by two dots, and so on.

46 20. The number of letters in the alphabet between the first and last letter of the place name, multiplied by ten.

47 7. Add the top and bottom numbers together, take the left one away from the right, and minus the results from each other.

48 4. Marbella. The others are; 1. Bermuda, 2. Martinique, 3. Trinidad, and 5. Barbados. Marbella is the only one not in the Caribbean.

49 C.

50 24ft. Add the alphanumeric values of the first and last letters of the tree's name. The date the tree was planted is a 'red herring'!

51 B. They all follow logical sequences of alphanumeric vales and numbers. However, B should be: (3 C) 6 9 (12 L) 15 (18 should be R not Q) and (21 U).

52 Michael Palin.

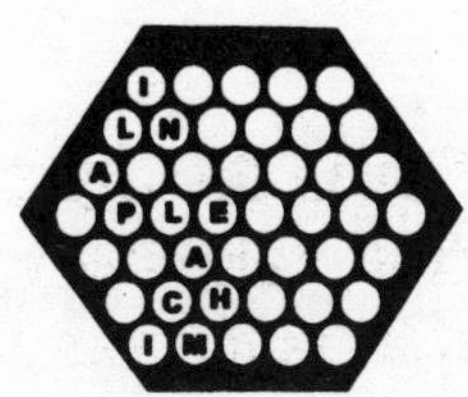

53 157. Take the second digit in each number, multiply it by itself, and add it to the original number.

54 39. Each number is the total of the alphanumeric values of the three corner letters in each box. The other letters don't count.

55 Top 33, Right 16, Bottom 9 and Left 5. From the twelve o'clock position the outer numbers subtract four as they go clockwise. The second row add four and the inner row subtract four. The number 4 in the centre is the clue.

56 31.

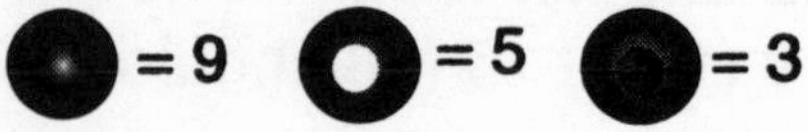

= 9 = 5 = 3

57 JU and AP. The letters are actually the first two letters of each of the first six months of the year, in reverse order.

58 4 (top) and 9 (bottom). Divide the grid into quarters. The four boxes in each quarter add up to 21.

59 Diamond 10 and Ruby 5. The vowels are worth 2 and the consonants are worth 1.

60 Examination. The circles are vowels in order (a=1, e=2, i=3 and so on) and the squares are consonants (b=1, c=2 and so on).

61 Rotherham.

62 63 and 32. Multiply the two outer numbers in each segment and put the answer in the opposite inner segment.

63 Alison. Each person's name begins with the last letter of another name, except Alison.

64 5–1. In each case take the alphanumeric values of the middle letter of the first word and the last letter of the second word.

65 40. E.g.,(9 x 4) + (7 - 3).

66 5. Add the number of consonants in the place name to the number of consonants in 'EUSTON': 2+3=5.

67 Chat shows. The third letter of each of Erica's 'likes' corresponds with each letter of her name in sequence.

68 4. Take the first digit of both 'Michael' and 'Maclean' and minus their alphanumeric values from each other, then do the same to the second digits and so on. The last digit in each name is ignored.

69 4. Greece Pound. Which should be Greece Drachma. The others were: 1. Holland Guilder, 2. Scotland Pound, 3. Belgium Franc, and 5. Italy Lira.

70 4 cm. Months with an even number of letters, half the number, those with an odd number, double the number.

71 B. A is the same as C and E, and D is the same as F.

72 A. The first column moves up one square at a time, the second moves down, the third up, and so on.

73 Chocolate. Starting with NK, N (alphanumeric value = 14) minus K (value 11) leaves 3 and 3 = C, and so on.

74 D.

75 B. The shape is reversed left to right, and the objects within it reverse tones.

76 510. E.g., 620 (6:20) – 110 (1:10) = 510.

77 879655. Starting with the word 'Chester' and working upwards to the word 'Computers', the number of letters in each word makes up the fax number. From 'Hypertec' to 'David', the number of letters in each word makes up the phone number.

78 Wallet, shoes, tie and jumper. Wallet is the odd one out. You don't wear a wallet.

79 △=3; □=4; ●=1. Each shape has a value equal to the number of its sides.

80 13. Letters with even alphanumeric values are worth four and the odd ones are worth three.

81 'Your cover has been blown. Await further instructions.' Each letter is replaced with the next but one in the alphabet.

82 9.55. Clock B moves on by 35 minutes, then it doubles to 70 minutes on Clock C, 140 on Clock D and 280 on Clock E.

83 54. Circle minus square multiplied by star: (8 - 2) x 9 = 54.

84 U. The letter I comes between H and J in the alphabet and U comes between T and V.

85 'I'm having a great time here in Tunisia. See you soon.' The message is actually back to front, with the last letter in the sentence becoming the first, and so on.

86 U and E. Each two letters are the last two of each colour of the rainbow.

87 D. B, D and J are all made up of both straight lines and curves. The others are either one or the other.

88 Rudolf Nureyev, Emily Bronte and Winston Churchill. Replace each vowel or consonant in the name with the one that follows it.

89 A. All of the bars match up and the numbers, when added to the barcode, add up to 74.

90 Carter 26 and Roosevelt 63. Starting with the first letter of the name, add together the alphanumeric values of every other letter.

91 27. Add the numbers in each row together, and divide the answer by the number of uncircled letters in the row: (7 + 29 + 45) ÷ 3 = 27.

92 7 and 2. Each two numbers are multiplied together and the three totals are added to make 63.

93 B.

94 Bottom 13 and side 13.

95 3. Fish finger. All the other names contain meat products: 1. Sausage roll, 2. Pork pie, 4. Black pudding, and 5. Roast beef.

96 Countdown.

		N		
D	T	U		
O	O			
	W	C		
		N		

97 Clare Short, William Hague, Alan Beith, Ann Winterton, John Prescott and Robin Cook.

98 3 and 4. Each number is the number of straight lines enclosing it. The circles do not count.

99 Three clicks left.

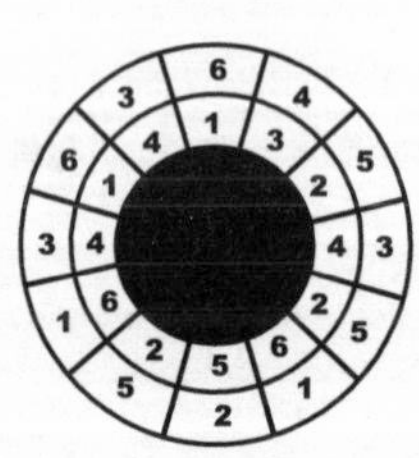

100 Gardeners' World. Take the first letter from the top arrow and the last from the bottom, then the second from the top and so on.

Part 2

1

What is the missing number?

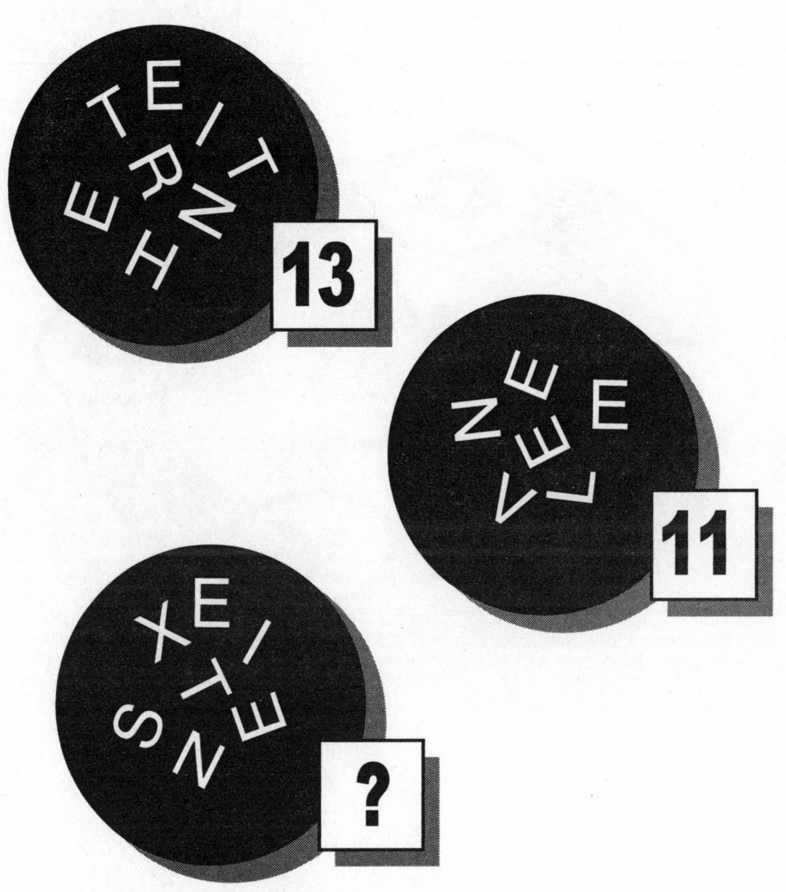

2

Which letter is next in this sequence?

3

How much has the dress been reduced in the sale?

4

Which sequence of 'stepping stones' (one from each row) should you use to get from A to B?

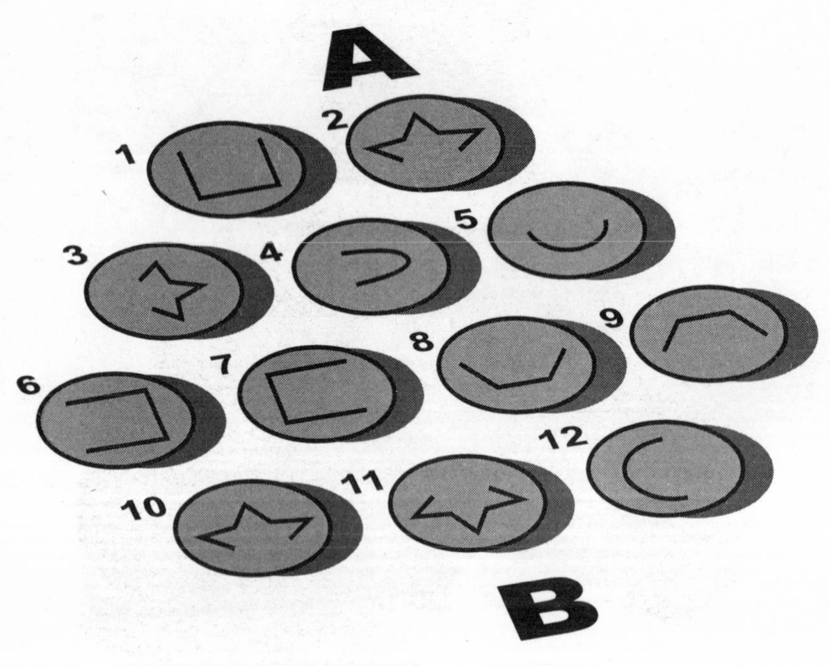

5

Which place is the odd one out?

6

What are the two missing numbers?

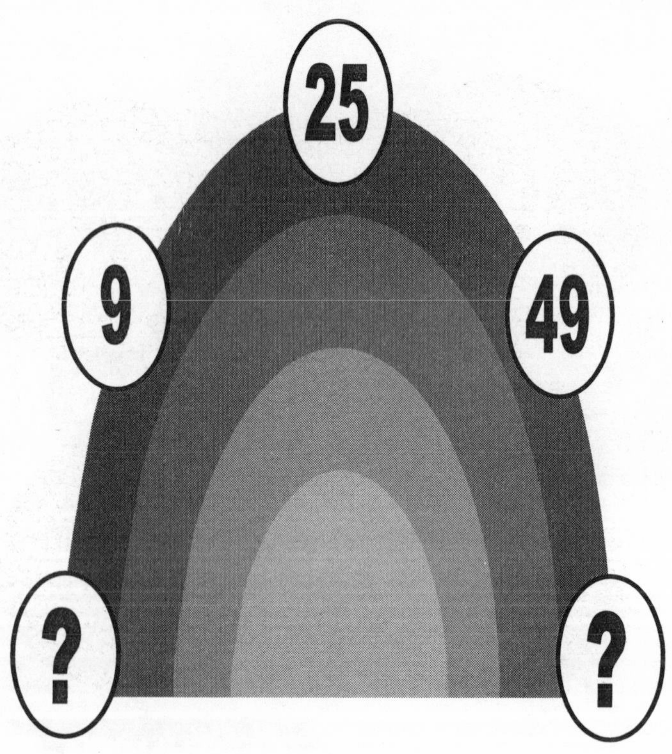

7

Which group of letters does not belong with the others?

8

Which of these seven shapes is the odd one out?

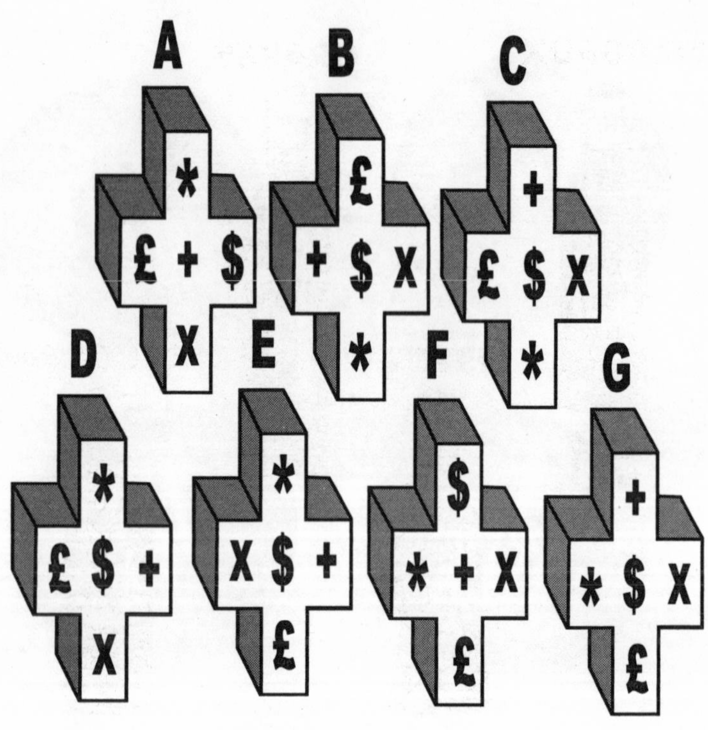

At a recent auction, the wines below were sold at the price shown per bottle.

How much was the Bergerac?

10

Join the letters together using straight lines, and without crossing over a line, to find the name of a TV detective.

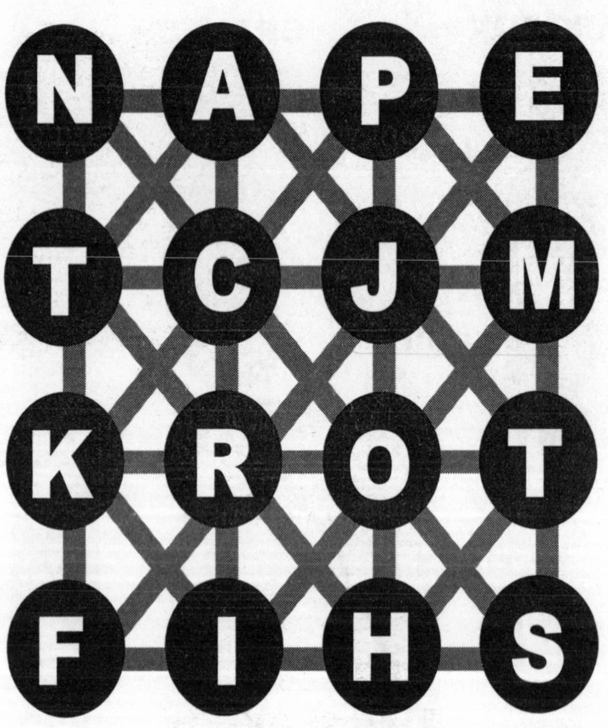

11

How much does it cost for a room in the Seaview Hotel this week?

12

Which author's name is the odd one out?

Which satellite will connect up these two communication centres?

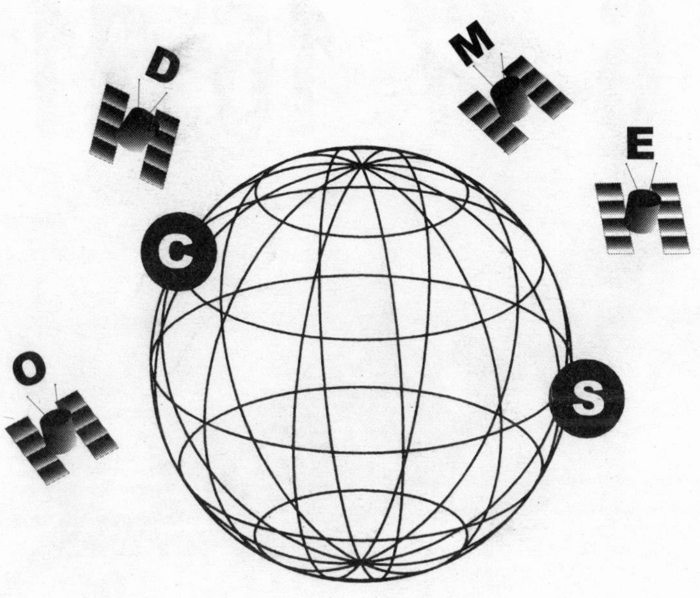

14

Which of these numbers should you add to open this combination lock?

6 17 16 21

15

Each of these cats has a strange name, but which is the odd one out?

16

Work out the number to replace the question mark.

17

Angela's favourite food is a hamburger. Ian's is pizza.

Does Simon like shortbread, chocolate or salad?

18

Which set of shapes does not belong with the others?

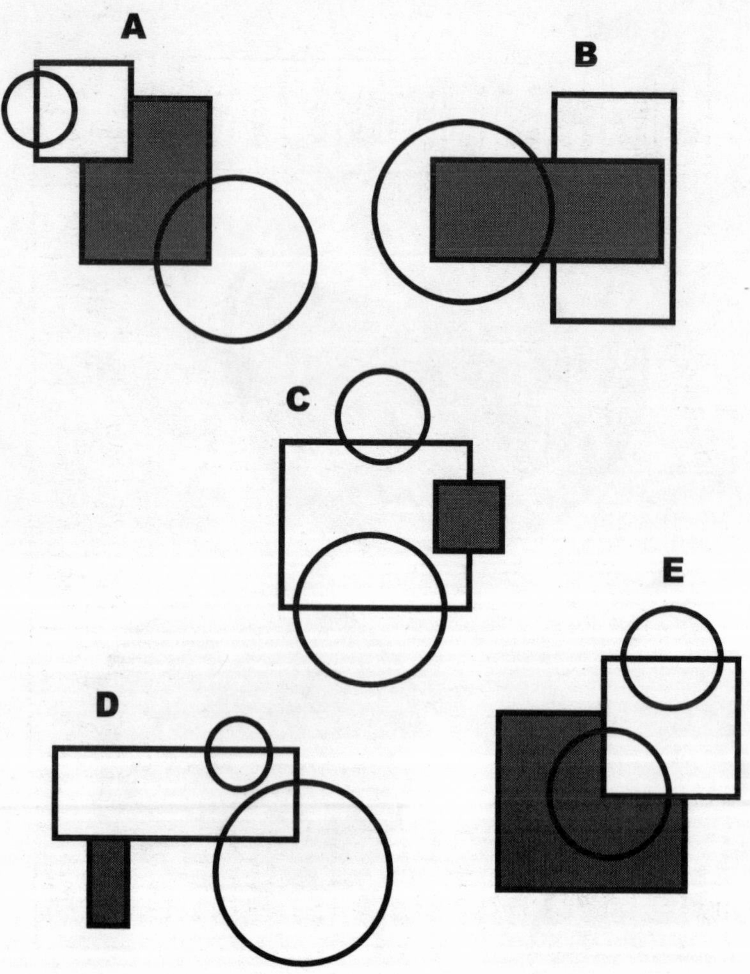

19

Which TV presenter is the odd one out?

JOHNLESLIE

LISATARBUCK

CAROL
VORDERMAN

JEREMYCLARKSON

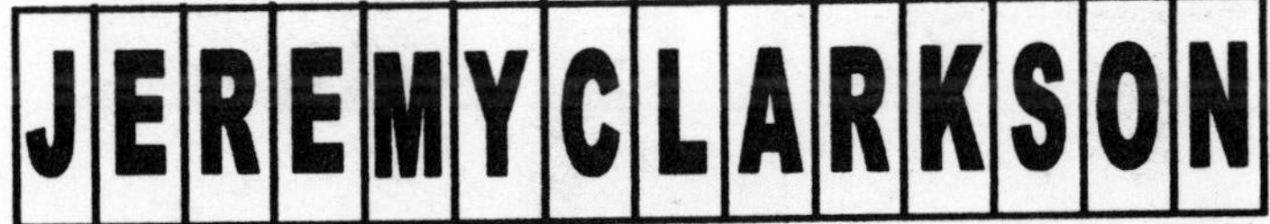

20

You want to order a bottle of wine,
but what is the price of the Meursault?

21

In a recent dice game, Nick threw a 2 and Julie threw a 4.

What did Helen throw?

22

Replace the question mark with a letter and then unravel each row to find the names of four drinks.

23

Which two numbers are needed to connect up this computer network?

24

You have received this e-mail, but there is a problem with your computer.

What does the message say?

eeaeaoouiieieoueiuth
rrmnypprtntsnthcmptr
ndstry...

25

At a party 48 people are drinking whiskey and 30 are drinking lager.

How many are drinking cider?

26

Which letter is missing from this grid?

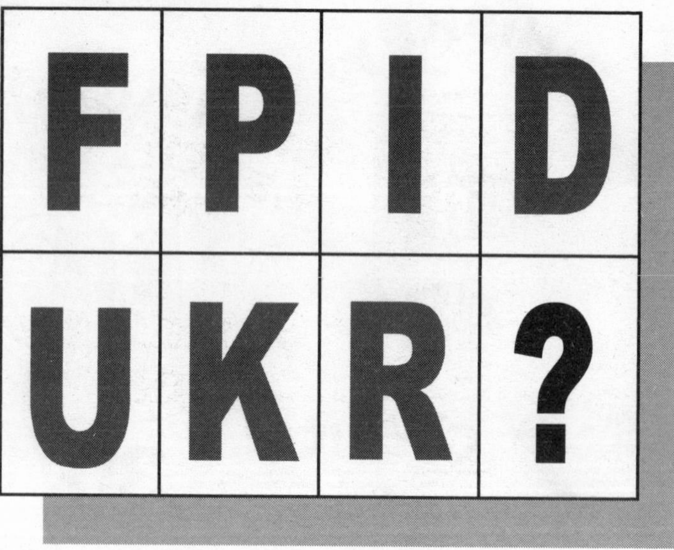

27

Shown below are the contents of this safe.

How many banknotes are there?

SHARE CERTIFICATES £7,000

JEWELLERY £1,800

BANKNOTES £?

A recent survey of geography teachers revealed that these were the most popular holiday destinations over the summer.

How many went to France?

GREECE	**25**
CANADA	**14**
POLAND	**12**
FRANCE	**?**

29

Which number should replace the question mark?

30

Which shape is the same as this one?

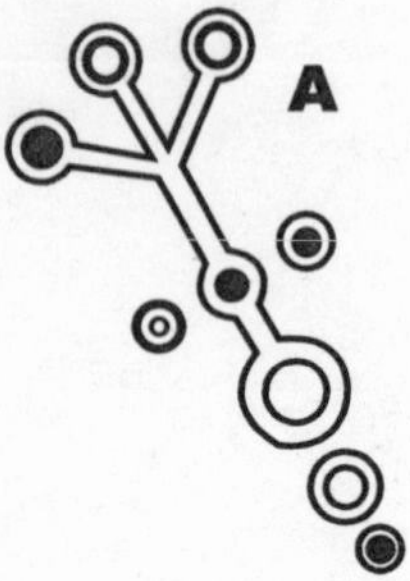

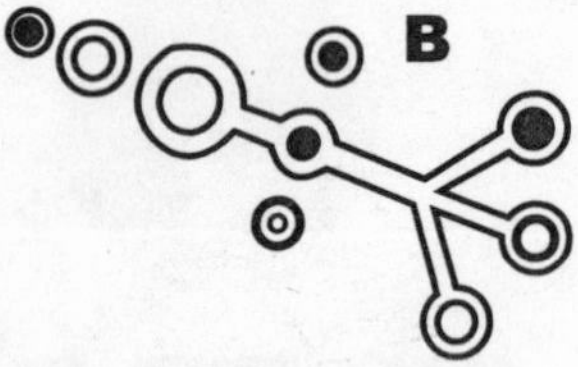

B

A

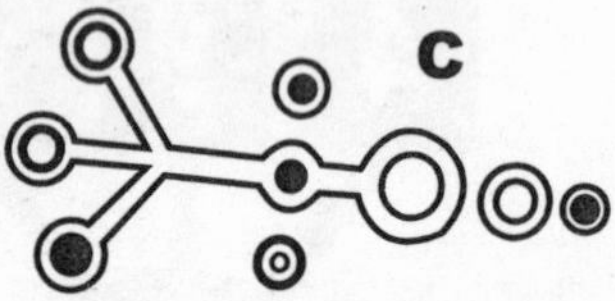

C

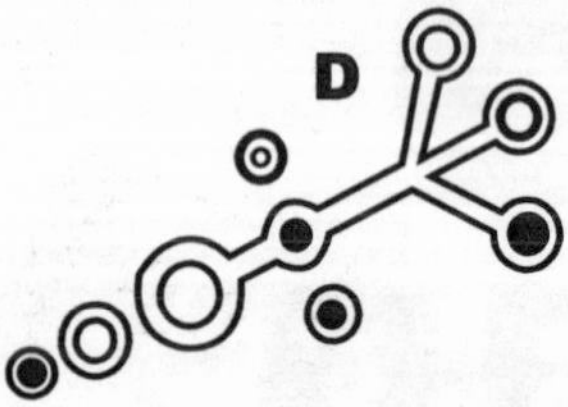

D

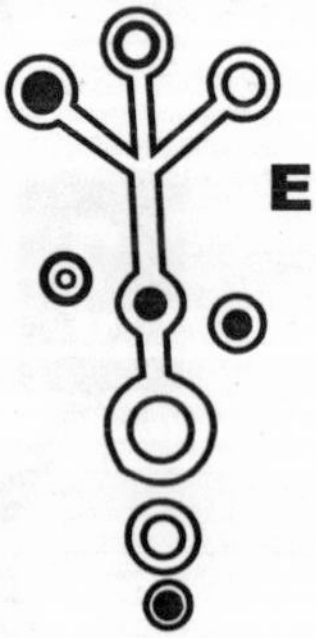

E

Which cracker does not belong with the others?

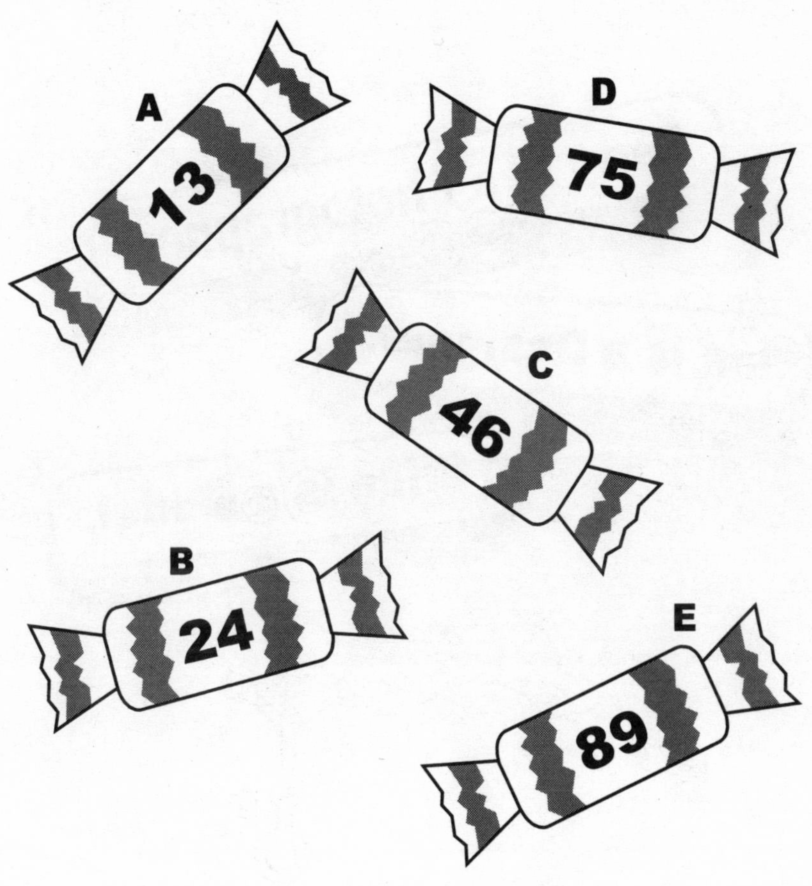

32

Is Rebecca a copywriter, illustrator or journalist?

Terry is a Photographer.

Ian is a Designer.

Erica is a Model.

33

What number should accompany the bottom row of balls?

Take one letter from each circle to spell out the name of an American 60s TV detective.

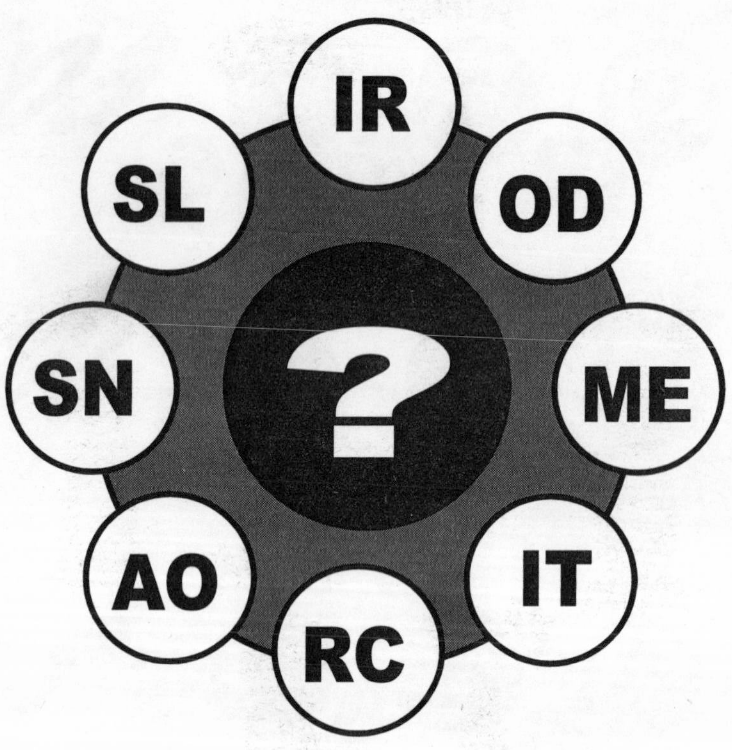

35

What are the values of the king and the pawn?

36

Last week, a freelance journalist worked these number of hours on these days.

How many hours did she work on Sunday?

37

Which shape does not belong with the others?

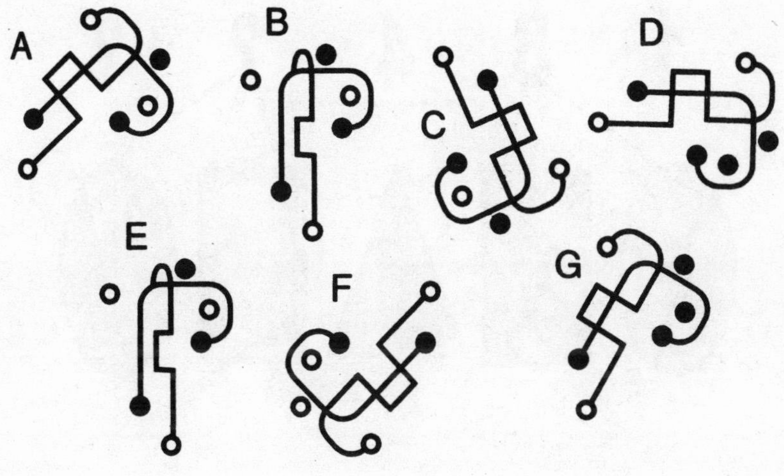

38

Fill in the two missing numbers.

39

A group of 100 people were surveyed to find out which soaps they watch.

How many watch Neighbours?

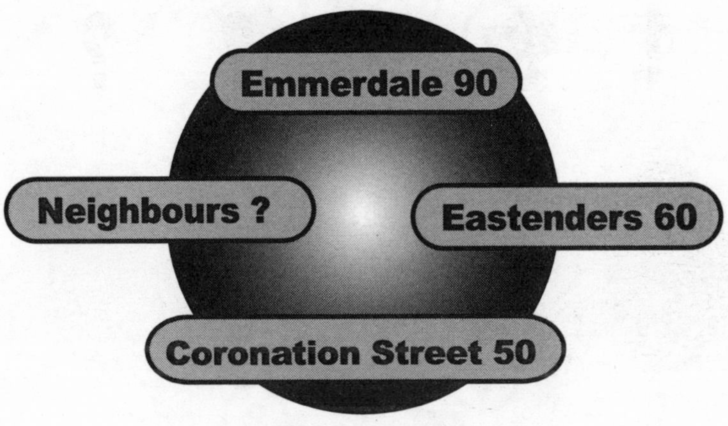

40

Which number should replace the question mark?

41

Below are six cities, with the number of local radio stations in each city.

How many are there in London and Newcastle?

42

When is Carolyn's birthday?

LINDSEY
DECEMBER 4th

ANDREAS
JANUARY 18th

DAVID
APRIL 22nd

CAROLYN
????

Yesterday, in a local bookshop, these numbers of hobby books were sold.

How many copies of Stamp Collecting?

TRAIN SPOTTING 9

WEB SURFING 16

STAMP COLLECTING ?

44

Which letter is missing?

45

What is the next number in the sequence?

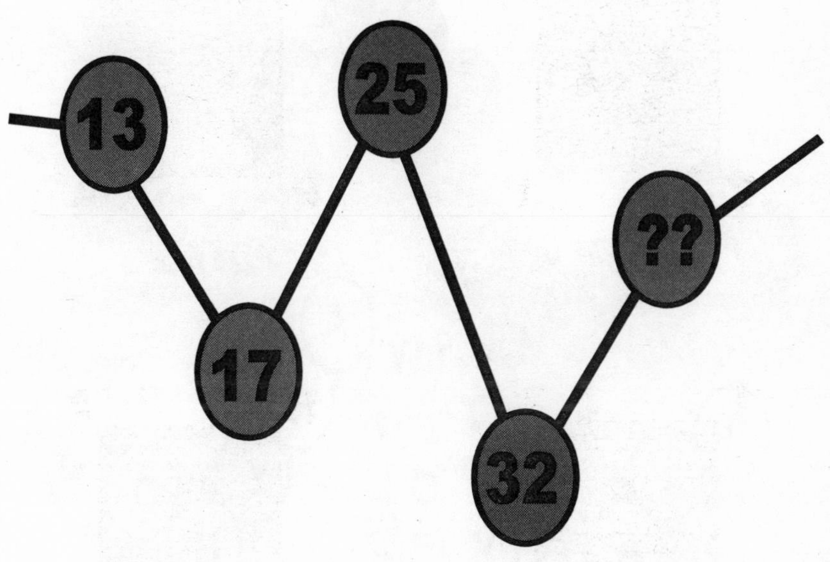

46

Which two television programmes are merged together here?

47

Add all the missing numbers to complete the grid so that each segment adds up to 30, and each ring adds up to 60.

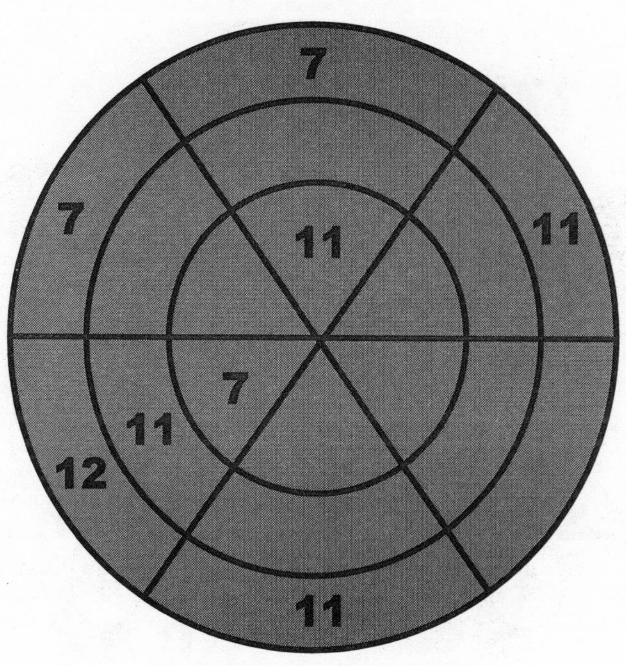

Lisa went to the sales and bought the following CDs.

Did she also buy Travis, Shania Twain or Oasis?

49

Can you replace the correct section of this map?

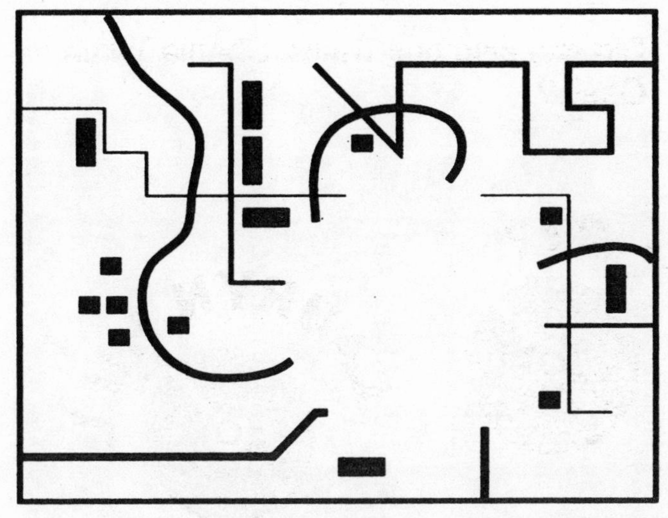

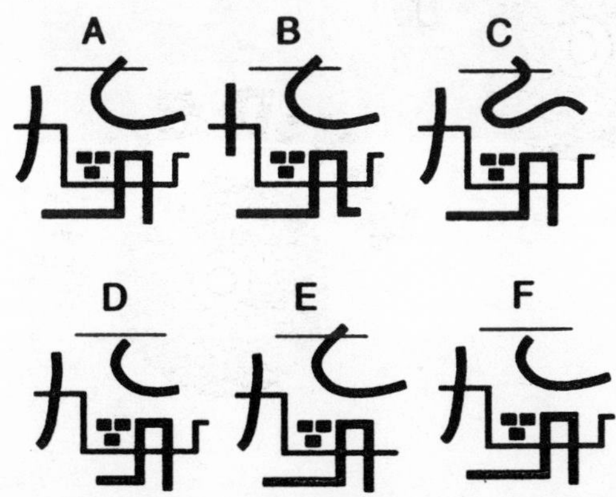

50

Which letter is missing?

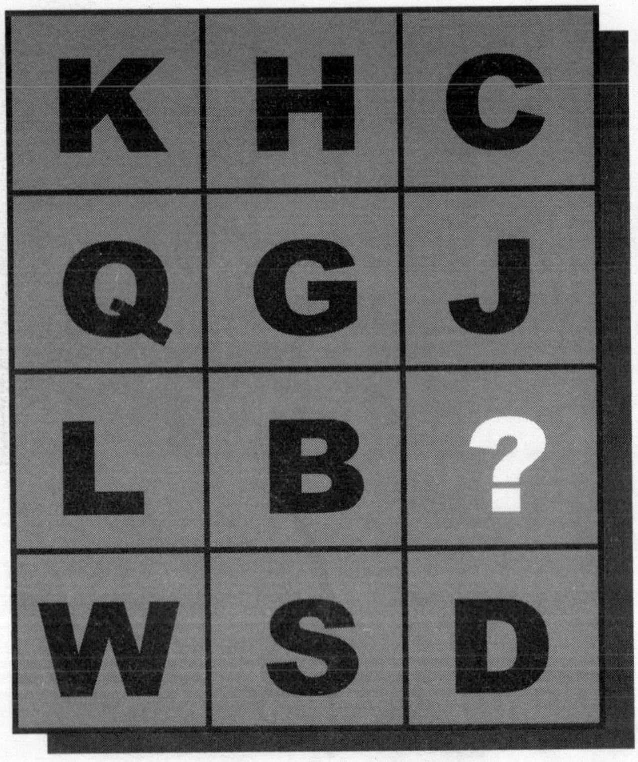

51

Can you fill in the missing number?

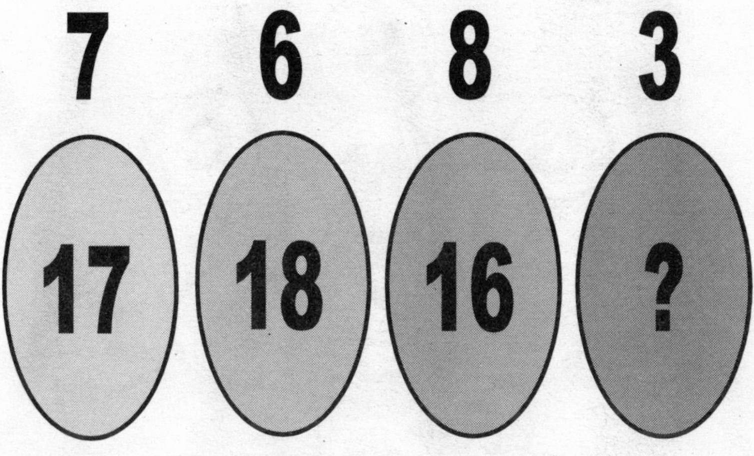

Put one letter in the middle, and rearrange the other letters so that each row spells out a five-letter word.

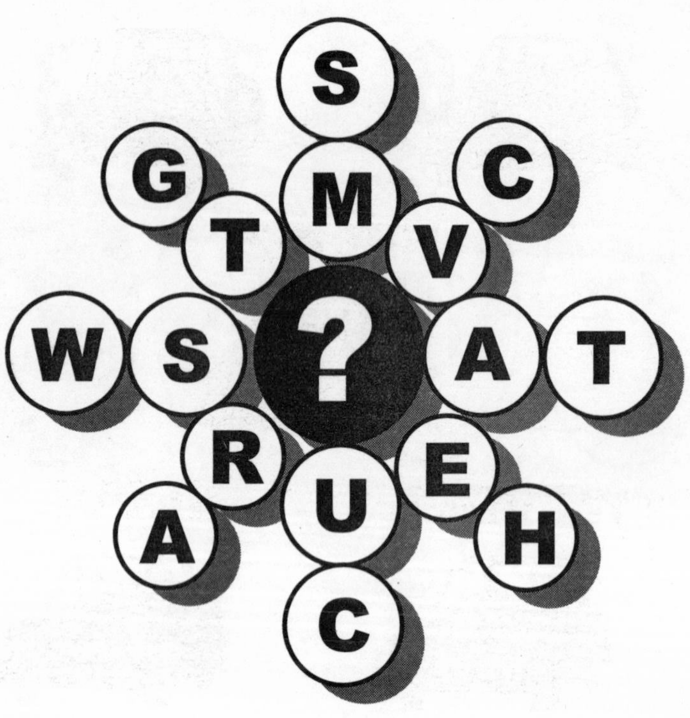

53

What are the five types of car in this car park?

54

Below are anagrams of five well-known TV detectives.

Work out who they are, and which is the odd one out.

55

Tina went to a party and drank the following drinks.

How many vodkas did she have?

56

Merged together in this grid are the names of two characters from the James Bond films.

Who are they?

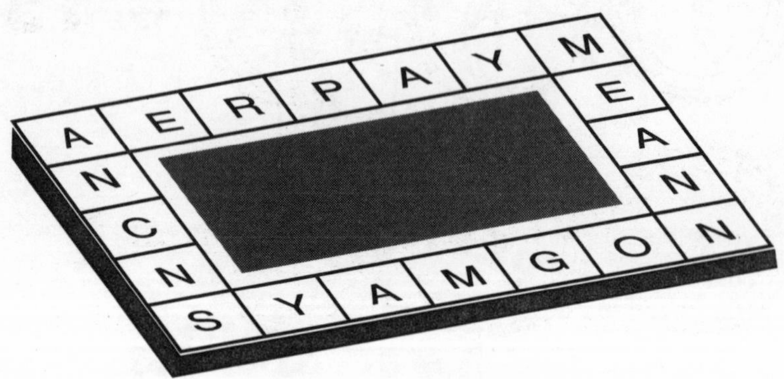

57

What is the missing number?

58

Which letter is next in this sequence?

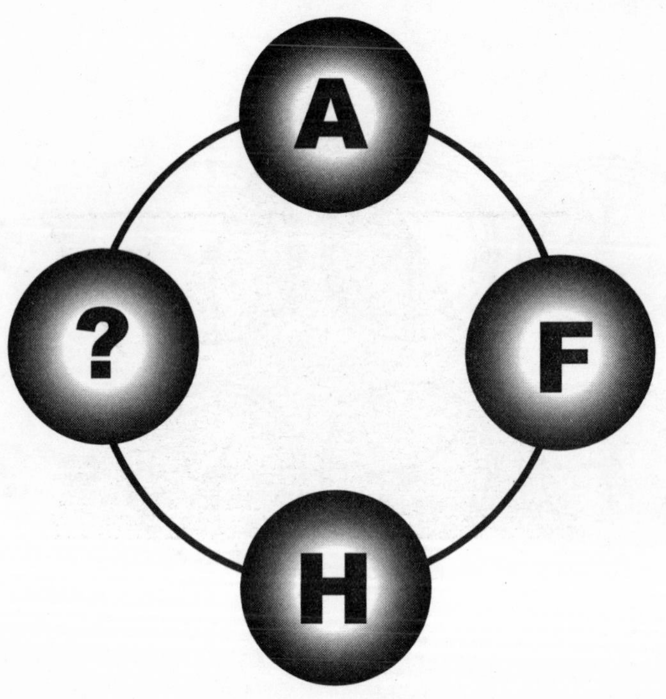

59

Which letter is missing?

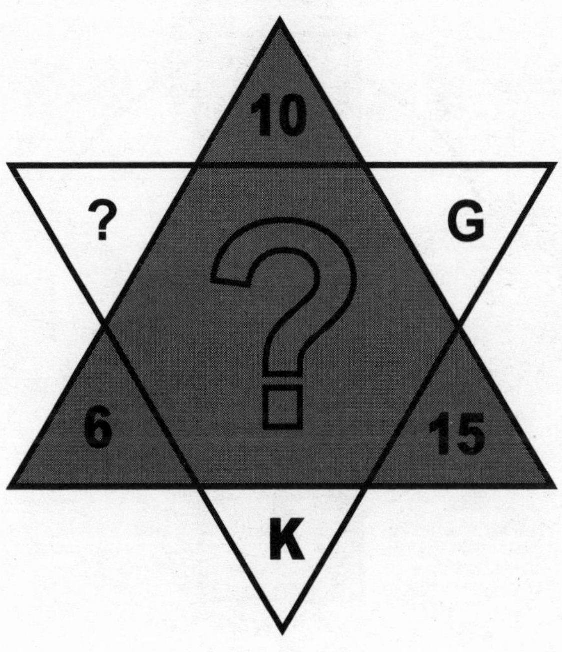

60

What is the missing number in this sequence?

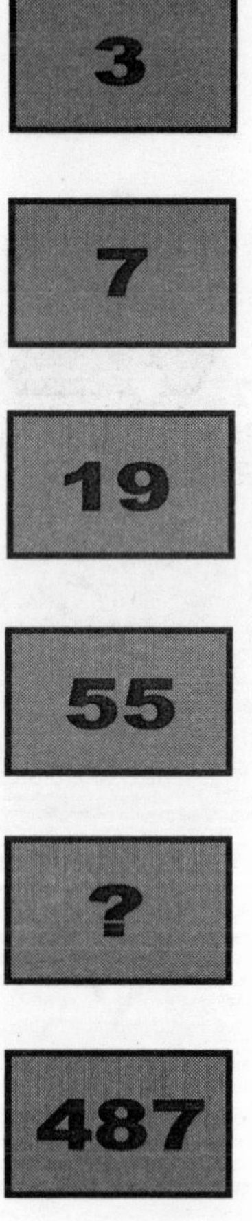

61

Which of these symbols does not belong in this sequence?

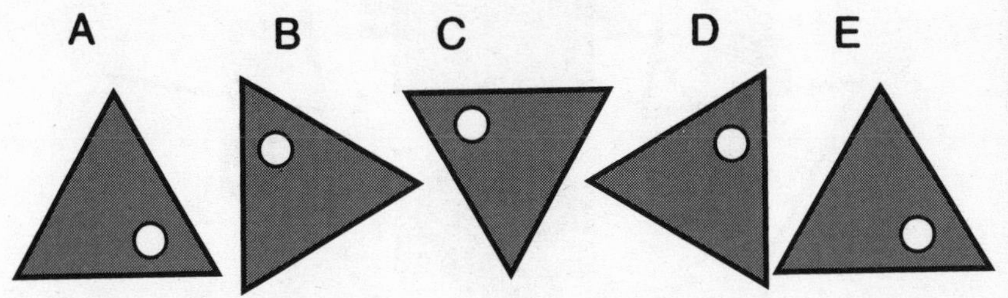

Using each letter only once, arrange them into an eight-letter word.

63

Which is the only key that fits this lock?

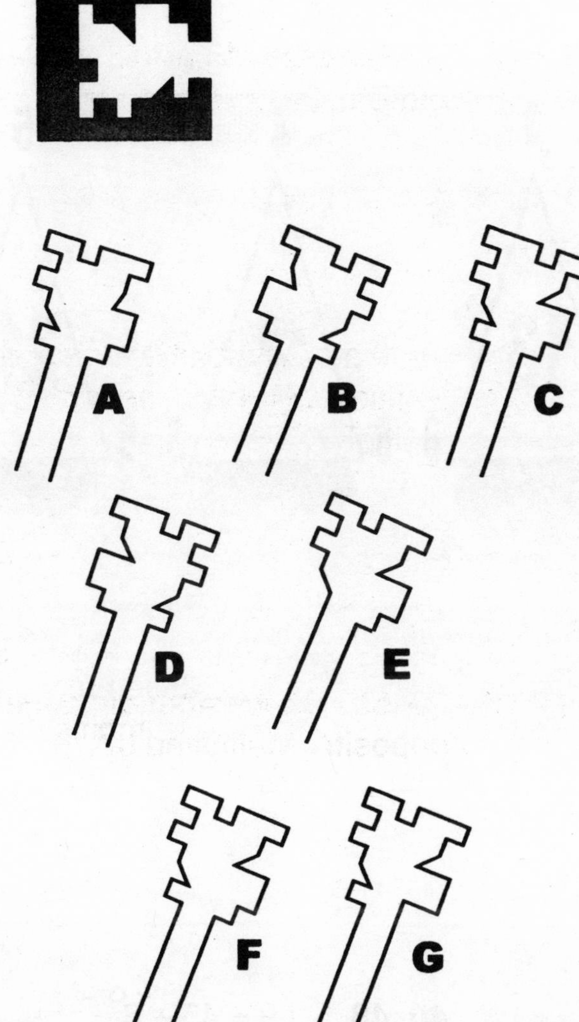

64

Can you work out the missing number?

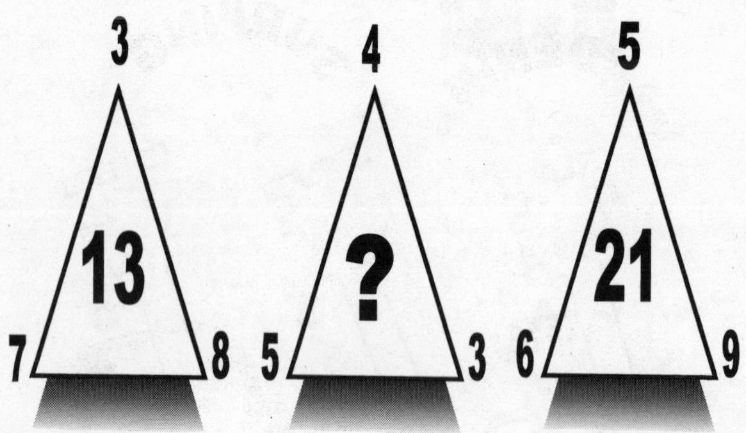

Michael's hobbies include the following.

Does he also like fishing, sailing or walking?

You arrive at a road junction and your car is low on fuel. You know from your map that it is 37 miles to Ashbury, 33 miles to Drayton and 20 miles to Whitefield.

How far is it to Kersal?

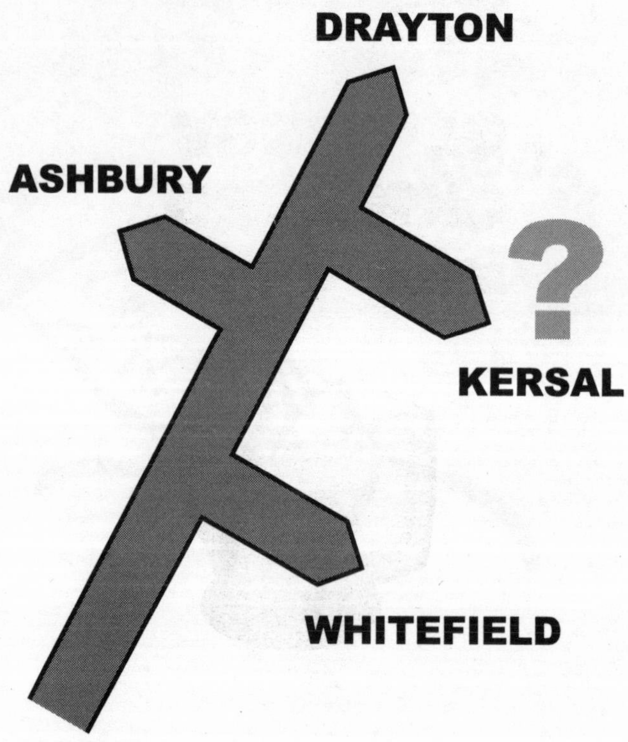

Here are the names of five well-known TV actors with the vowels missing and the other letters mixed up.

Who are they?

BSNR RNG
LCHML LCLNS
GLN HRSV
CKN RYRB
MND TBNR

68

Pennsylvania State Prison in the USA has a strange way of numbering its prisoners.

What is the prison number of John 'Mad Dog' Freeman?

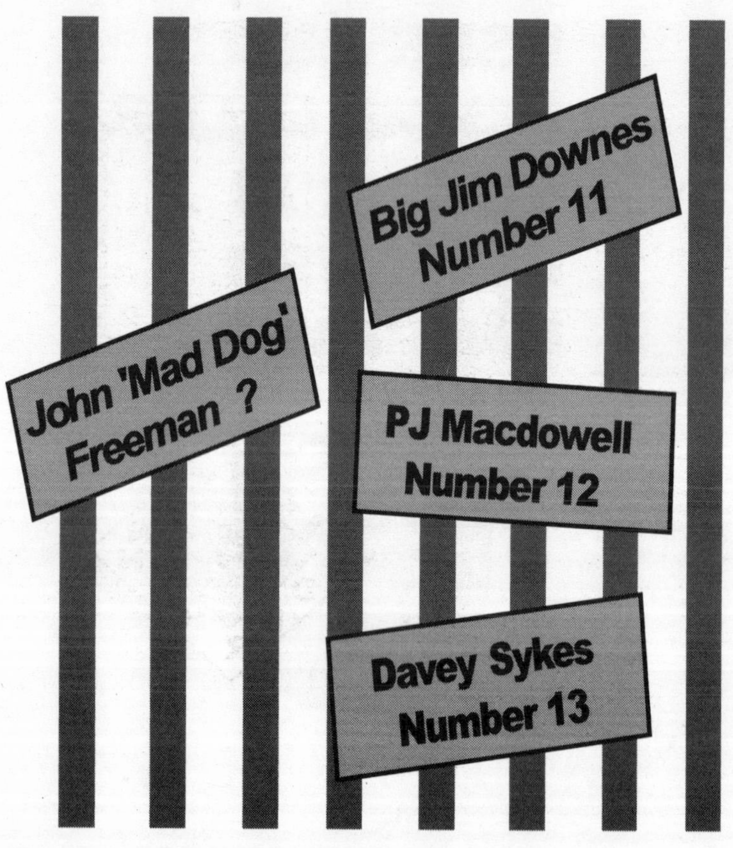

69

Who are these four politicians?

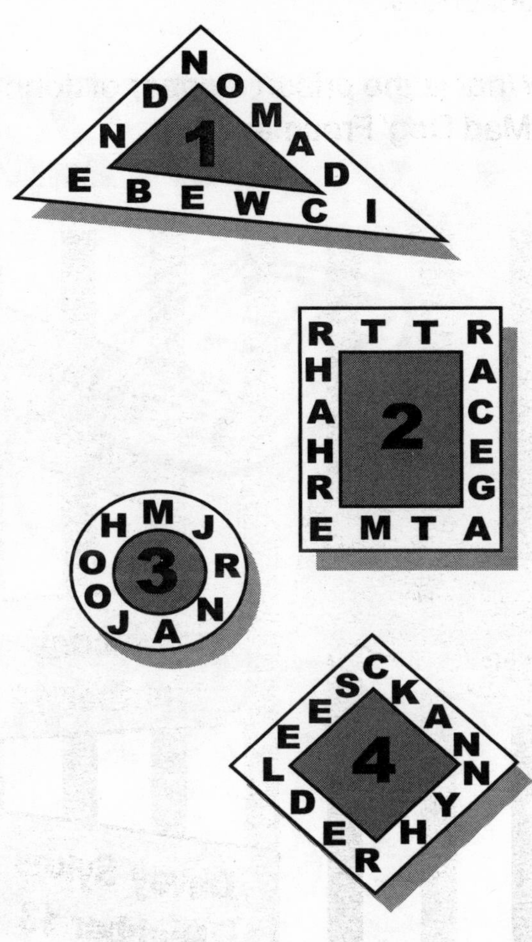

70

Find the pattern in the letters to complete the telephone number.

? 9 15 22

71

If ◆✲✡✳☆✥✲ is Frasier, what are these other television programmes?

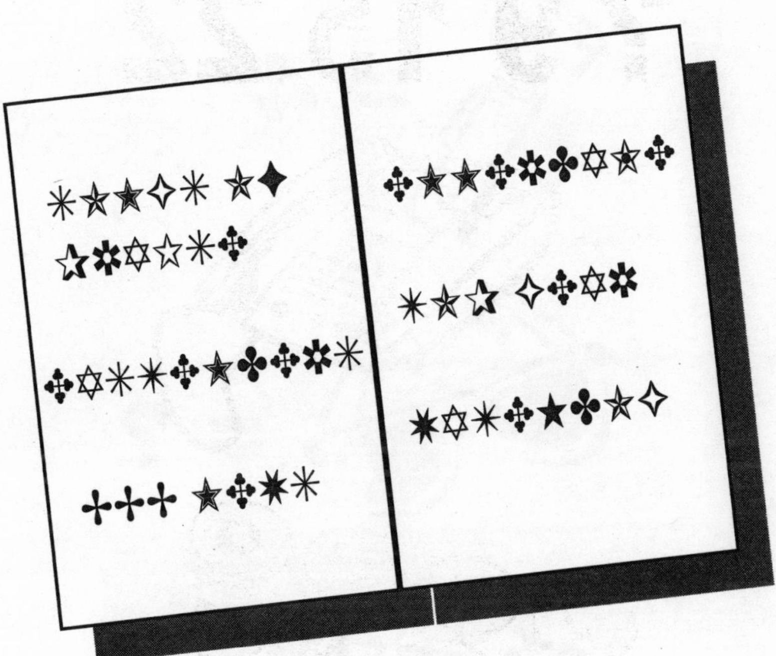

72

If the torch is 4 and the camera is 3, what is the value of the sunglasses?

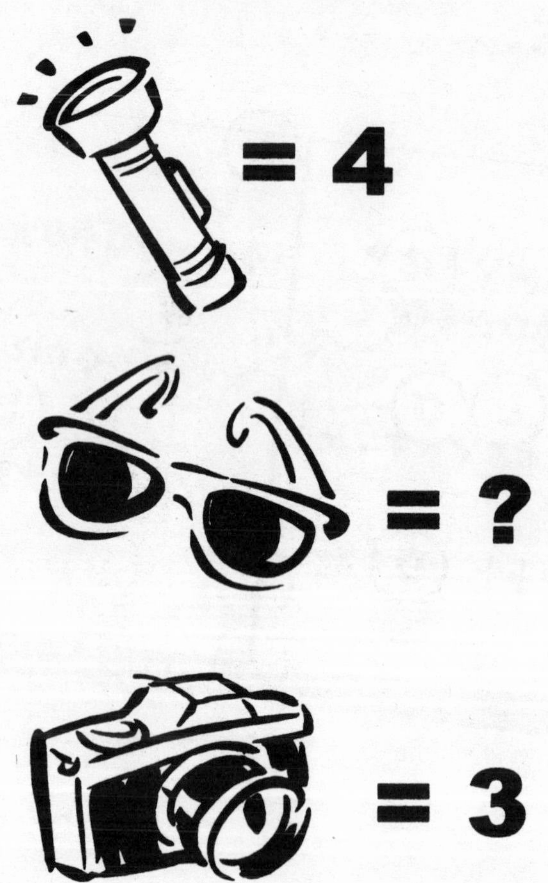

73

Starting from the centre, pick one letter from each point of the star to spell out the title of a television programme.

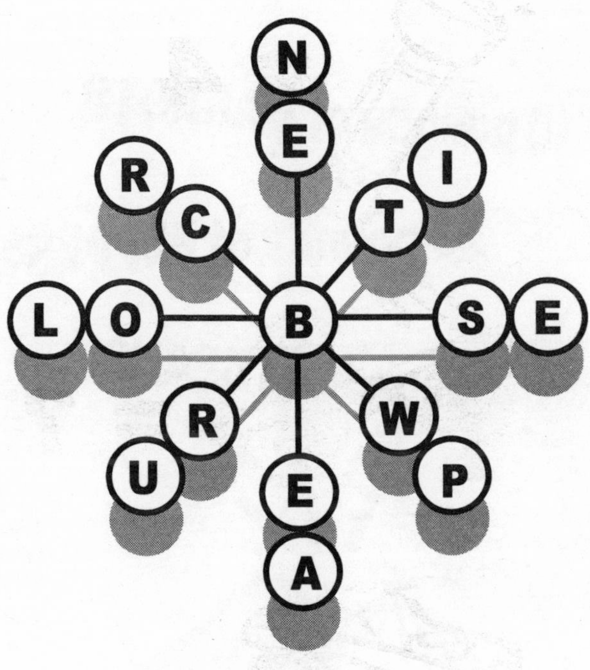

Every Saturday, a restaurant buys the following vegetables from the market.

But how many pounds of onions do they buy?

10 pounds of CARROTS

23 pounds of PEPPERS

7 pounds of BEANS

75

Where should the dot be in the last grid?

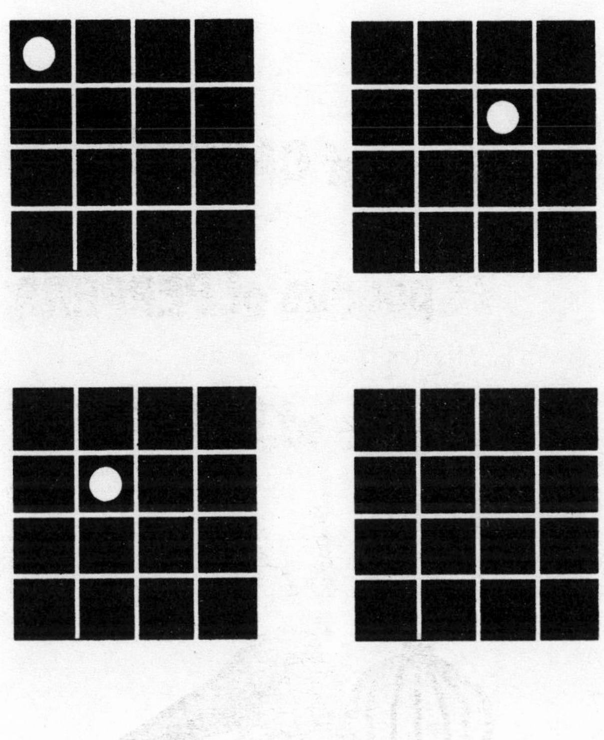

76

How far away are Amsterdam and Geneva?

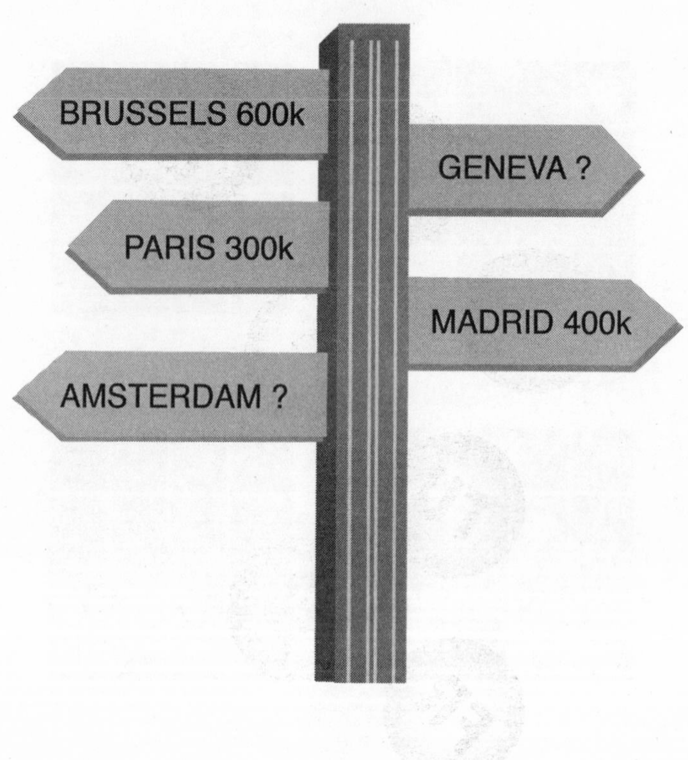

77

Which two letters are missing from the circles?

78

Break time in the office ... 15 people drink coffee and 20 drink tea.

How many drink cocoa?

Which symbol is missing from the sequence below?

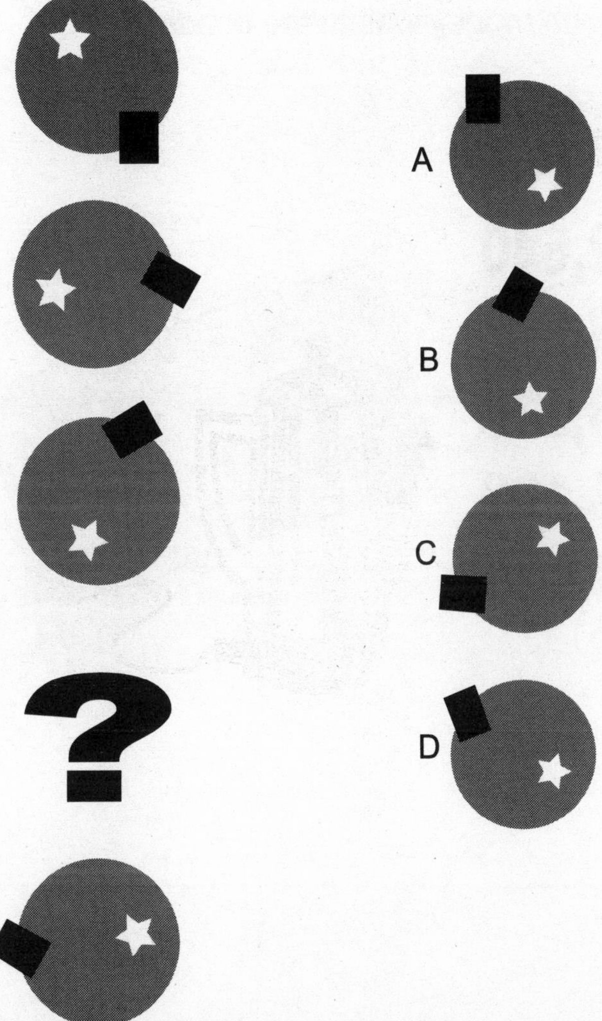

Detectives have unearthed the proceeds of a robbery. It is a bundle of £20 notes numbered consecutively from 637912 to 638106.

How much money was in the bundle?

A. £2,640
B. £3,800
C. £3,920
D. £4,100
E. £4,020

81

If χοϖεντρψ is Coventry, what are these other UK place names?

σηεφφιελδ

μανχηεστερ

γλασγοω

βλαχκποολ

πορτσμουτη

Work out the missing number.

6	4	4	1	6	1
8	2	3	5	1	9
2	8	3	3	4	7
1	1	2	2	3	3
5	3	2	3	4	?

83

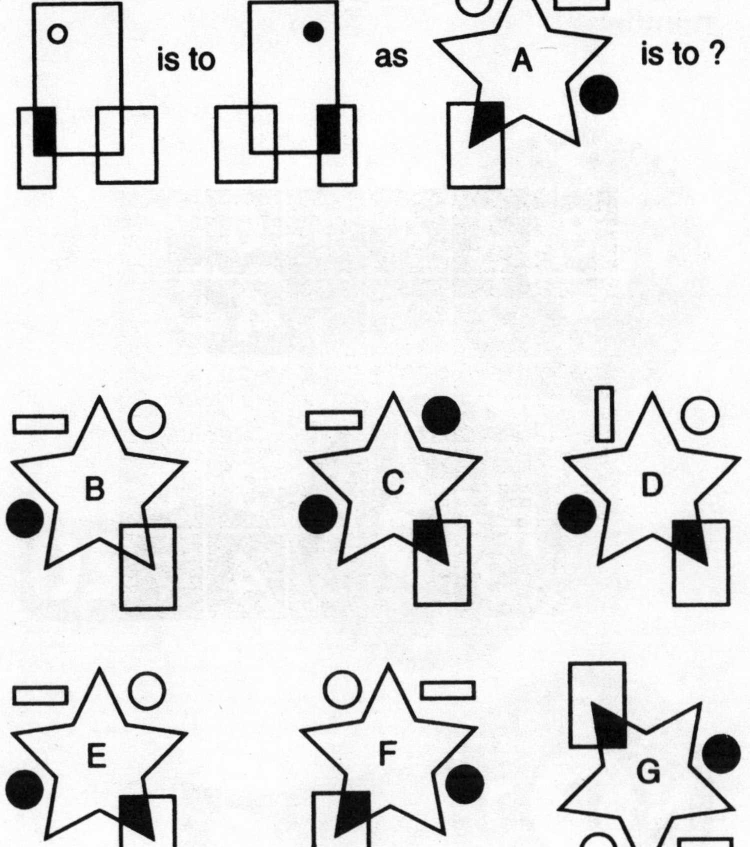

Replace the question mark with the correct number.

85

You have received this e-mail from agent ‘K’.

What does it say?

Wood wo kd dro rydov yx Pbsnki.

Osqrd y’mvymu.

There have been redundancies at the local council offices.

How many from the tourism department?

87

Key in the missing letter.

88

Donald keeps his precious metals collection in his safe.

How many pieces of gold does he have?

SILVER
GOLD
PLATINUM

89

Add the final letter.

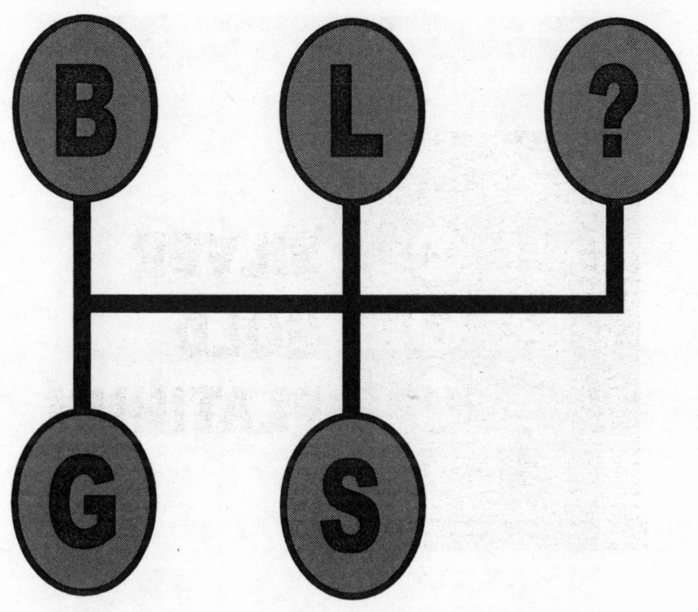

90

What number is missing from column four?

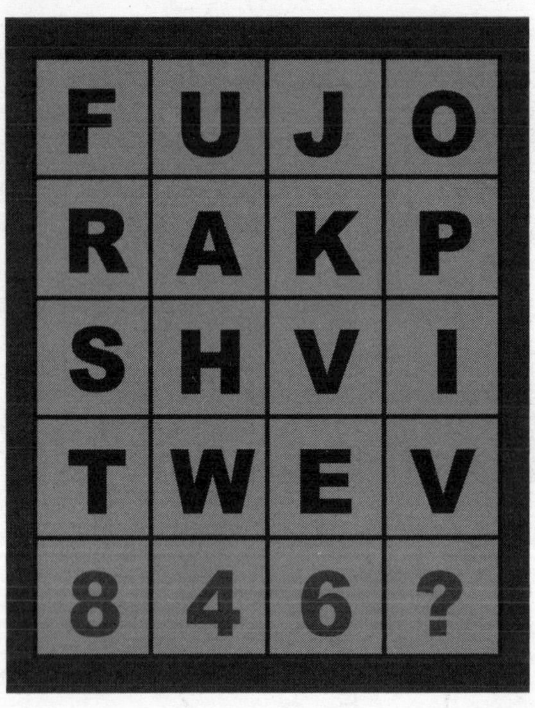

91

Which shape is identical to the one below?

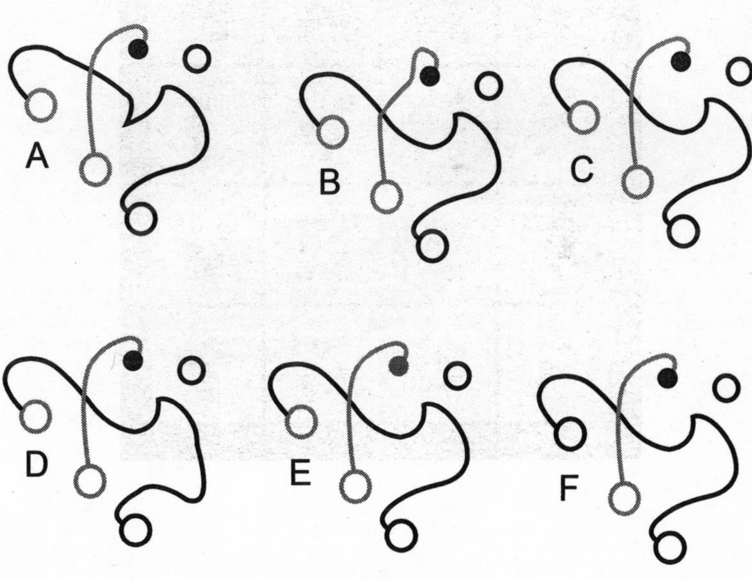

92

Which child's name is the odd one out?

93

What number goes with the letter P?

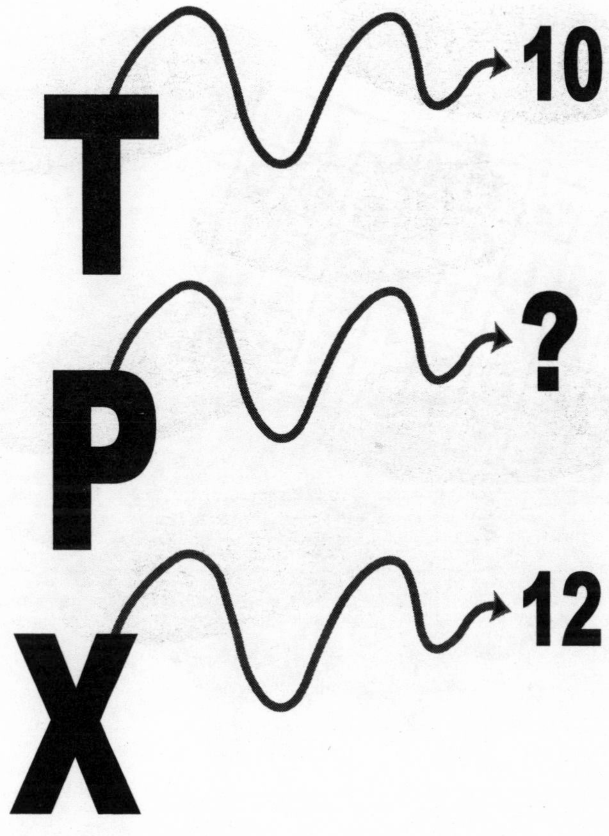

94

In the grid below are Michigan, Chicago, Seattle, Florida and Ohio. The remaining letters spell out another place in the USA.

Where is it?

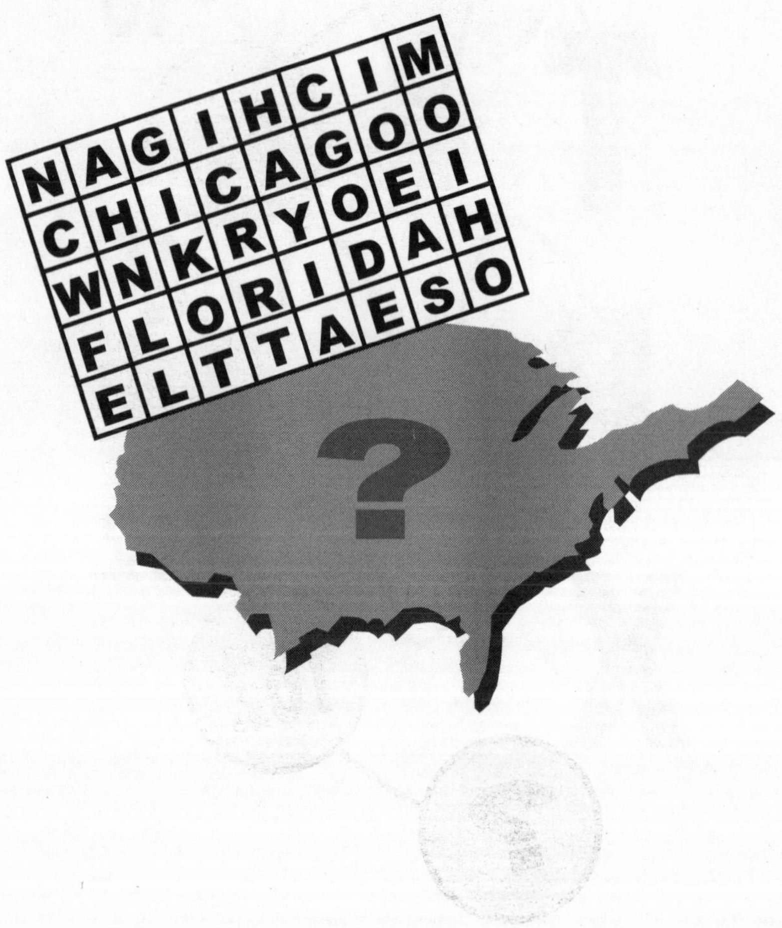

Find the next number in the sequence.

96

Which shape does not belong with the others?

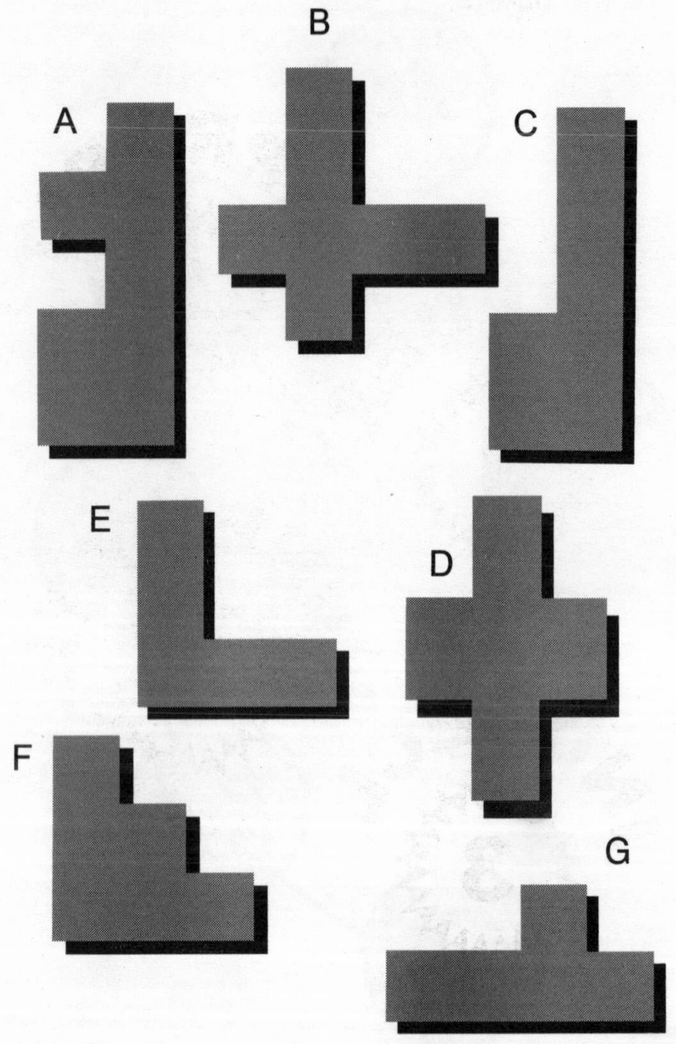

Unravel these anagrams, and then decide which word does not fit with the others.

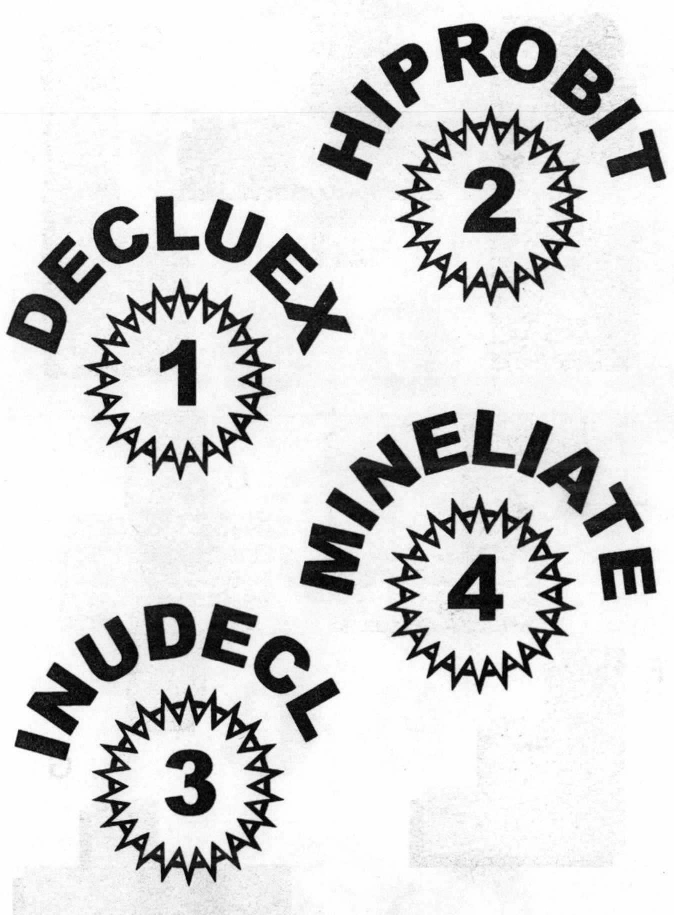

Add the missing number.

99

Trevor's friends live in these places.

But does *he* live in Sheffield, Nottingham or Liverpool?

***PAUL*- MANCHESTER**

***SHELENA*- BRISTOL**

***JOHN*- ORMSKIRK**

What is Eric Nutter's prison number?

Solutions

1 16. Rearrange the letters in each circle to spell the number.

2 Q. Each letter is the next but one after each of the first four vowels.

3 £27.00. Take the alphanumeric values of the first three letters of each item and add them together.

4 1, 5, 8 and 11. All of these symbols are open at the top.

5 Leeds. All of the place names contain two vowels, but only Leeds has two the same.

6 1 and 81. 1 x 1=1, 3 x 3 = 9, 5 x 5 = 25, 7 x 7 = 49, 9 x 9 = 81.

7 SWD. The others are all fruits with the vowels missing: peach, apple, tomato and mango. SWD is swede, which is a vegetable.

8 C is the odd one out. A is the same as F, B is the same as E, and D is the same as G.

9 £16. Take the alphanumeric value of the first letter of the wine and multiply it by the last number in the date.

10 Jack Frost.

11 £51. Prices work out at £17 per star.

12 Margaret Drabble. It's the only name that doesn't begin with a vowel.

13 O. Letters S and C have no straight lines and neither has O.

14 17. 5, 13, 11 and 17 are all prime numbers.

15 A. The names are anagrams of: orange, buttercup, primrose, nettle and daisy. Orange is the only fruit.

16 6. Add together the four numbers at the top, bottom, right and left points, then add together the remaining four numbers, and subtract them from the first total.

17 Chocolate. The number of consonants in each choice equals the number of letters in each person's name.

18 C. All of the other arrangements have three lines enclosed inside circles. This one only has two.

19 Carol Vorderman. Her name contains five vowels while the others contain four.

20 £7. The alphanumeric values of the first and last letters in the name. Subtract one from the other.

21 5. The score is the number of letters in the alphabet between the first and the last latter of each name.

22 E. Sherry, bitter, claret and coffee.

23 7 and 2. Each two numbers are multiplied together and the three totals are added to make 63.

24 'There are many opportunities in the computer industry'. All the vowels and consonants are in word order. Slot the vowels into the consonants in the correct places to read the message.

25 21. Each number is the combined sum of the alphanumeric value of the first and last letter in each drink.

26 W. F is 6 from the start of the alphabet and U is 6 from the end. P is 16 from the start, K is 16 from the end and so on...

27 £1,800. Multiply the number of consonants by the number of vowels, and add two noughts.

28 14. Muliply the alphanumeric values of the middle two letters in the name.

29 22. 3 x 9 = 27- 5 = 22

30 C.

31 D. All of the others have a smaller first number.

32 Journalist. In each example the first letter of the name is the same as the fourth letter of the profession.

33 51. In each row, the top numbers are taken away from each other; 8-4-1 = 3. The bottom numbers are added together; 6+2+9 = 17. The results are multiplied.

34 Ironside.

35 King 3, pawn 1. Each vowel is given a number corresponding to its order. A=1, E=2, I=3, O=4, U=5. The numbers of each vowel in each name are added together.

36 7. The number of hours is actually the number of letters from the first letter of the day to the end of the alphabet.

37 F. A is the same as C, B is the same as E, and D is the same as G.

38 6 and 1. A circle means divide the number by itself, a square means add, and a triangle multiply.

39 60. The number of consonants in the soap opposite, multiplied by 10.

40 48. 5 x 9 = 45 + 3.

41 London = 13 and Newcastle = 11. The number of letters in the alphabet between the first letter of the city and Z.

42 March 15th. The month is the alphanumeric value of the first letter, and the day is the middle letter of the name.

43 25. Take away the number of letters in the first word from those in the second word, then multiply the remainder by itself.

44 B. Zebra. (Tiger, panda, whale.) They are all mammals.

45 37. In each circle, add the two numbers together and move on by that amount.

46 Wish You Were Here and Ready, Steady, Cook. The first letter from the top one, the second from the bottom, and so on...

47 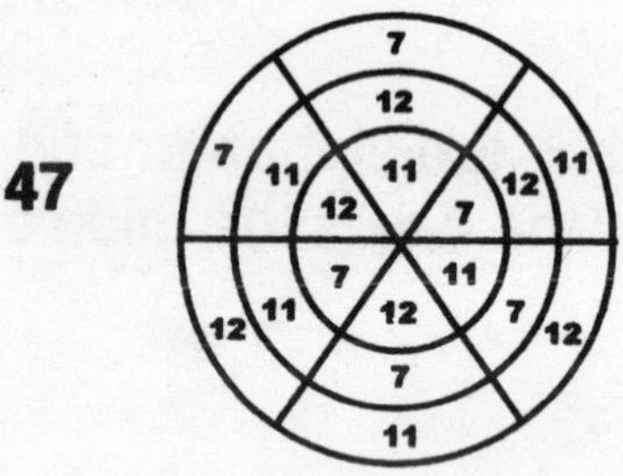

48 Oasis. Each letter in the name Lisa is three letters in front of the first letter of each band name: L – Oasis, I – Lauryn Hill, S – Vengaboys and A – David Bowie.

49 A.

50 J. From left to right in each row, find the alphanumeric value of the first two letters and take the second from the first to find the third. L (12) minus B (2) = J (10).

51 21. The number in each circle is the total of all the top numbers, except the one directly above it.

52 I. Music, waist, eight and vicar.

53 Jaguar, Ford, Skoda, Daewoo and Rover. Count from Z in the alphabet to each letter, then count that number in from A to find each correct letter.

54 Miss Marple, Inspector Morse, Chief Inspector Wexford, Columbo and Hercule Poirot. The odd one out is Miss Marple as she is the only woman.

55 1. The number of letters in the alphabet that come between the 'T' in Tina and the first letter of each drink.

56 Moneypenny and Scaramanga.

57 14. Add together the numbers which the small hand is pointing to in the two outside clocks, then take away the small-hand number in the middle one.

58 K. The sequence is made up of the first four capital letters that are made up of three straight lines.

59 P. Each number is the alphanumeric value of the opposite letter, minus one.

60 163. Each number is multiplied by three, and then two is taken off to get the next number in the sequence.

61 B. The sequence moves 90 degrees right each time. This one is a mirror image of what it should be.

62 Morphine.

63 F.

64 17. (5 x 4) - 3 = 17.

65 Fishing. The middle letter (H) continues the sequence. Gardening (E), surfing (F) and jogging (G).

66 6 miles. Add together the alphanumeric values of the second letter and the second to last letter in each place.

67 Robson Green, Michelle Collins, Nigel Havers, Nick Berry and Amanda Burton.

68 Number 6. Take the number of letters in the name away from the number of letters in 'Pennsylvania State Prison'.

69 1. Ann Widdecombe 2. Margaret Thatcher 3. John Major 4. Charles Kennedy.

70 4. Diagonally from the bottom right, V is the 22nd letter of the alphabet, O the 15th, I the 9th and D the 4th.

71 Songs of Praise, Eastenders, BBC News, Emmerdale, Top Gear and Watchdog.

72 7. The number of consonants in the word.

73 Blue Peter.

74 21 pounds of onions. The alphanumeric value of the first letter added to the number of letters.

75 Top right square. First corner one in, second corner two in, third corner three in and last corner four in.

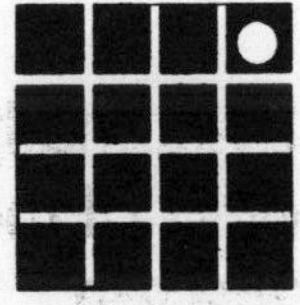

76 Geneva = 300k and Amsterdam = 600k. Take the number of vowels from the number of letters in the word, and multiply by 100.

77 MO and WE. The circles contain the first two letters of each of the days of the week.

78 6. Add together the alphanumeric values of all the consonants in each word.

79 A. Each shape rotates 60 degrees anticlockwise.

80 C.

81 SHEFFIELD, MANCHESTER, GLASGOW, BLACKPOOL and PORTSMOUTH.

82 2. The two outside columns add up to 22, the next two add up to 18 and the middle two add up to 14.

83 E.

84 36. Each number is made by adding the alphanumeric values of only the centre and the right-hand letters.

85 'Meet me at the hotel on Friday. Eight o'clock.' 'K' is the clue... A becomes K, B becomes L, and so on.

86 10. Each vowel in the word is worth 2, and each consonant is worth 1.

87 U. The alphanumeric values of each two letters across when added together make up the alphanumeric value of the third letter.

88 2. The number of letters in the alphabet between D (for Donald) and the first letter of the metal.

89 Z. B is the letter next to the first vowel, A, G is one letter from E, L is two letters from I, S three letters from O and Z four letters from U.

90 4. In each column consonants are worth 2, and vowels are worth 0.

91 C.

92 Katie. This name contains three vowels. All of the others contain two.

93 8. Each number is half the alphanumeric value of the letter.

94 New York.

95 243. Each number moves on by half its amount.

96 D. All of the other shapes are asymmetrical.

97 3. The words are: 1 – exclude, 2 – prohibit, 3 – include, and 4 – eliminate.

98 21. Multiply the top two numbers, add the left one, then subtract the number on the right.

99 Sheffield. The first letter of each place name follows on from the last letter of the person's name.

100 2312354023. Add together the alphanumeric values of each two letters in the name.

Part 3

1

Which number is needed to complete this computer network?

Replace the question mark with a letter and then unravel each row to find four fruits.

3

Take one letter from each circle to spell out the name of an important European City.

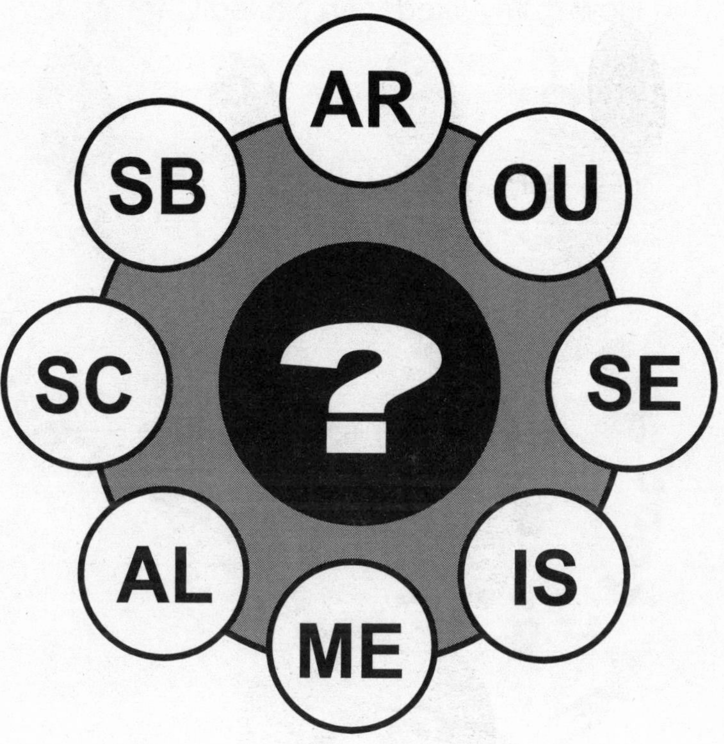

4

A group of people were surveyed to find out which were their favourite cookery programmes.

How many liked 'The Naked Chef'?

5

Add all the missing numbers to complete the grid so that each segment adds up to 29, and each ring adds up to 58.

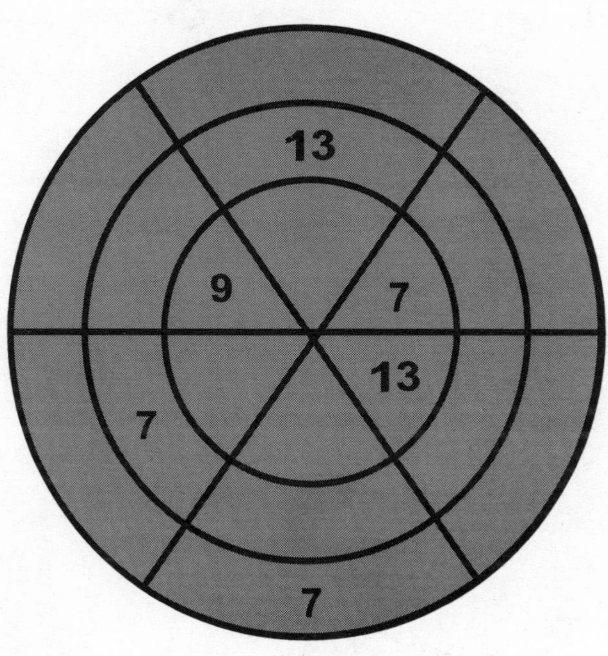

6

Which shape is not identical to this one?

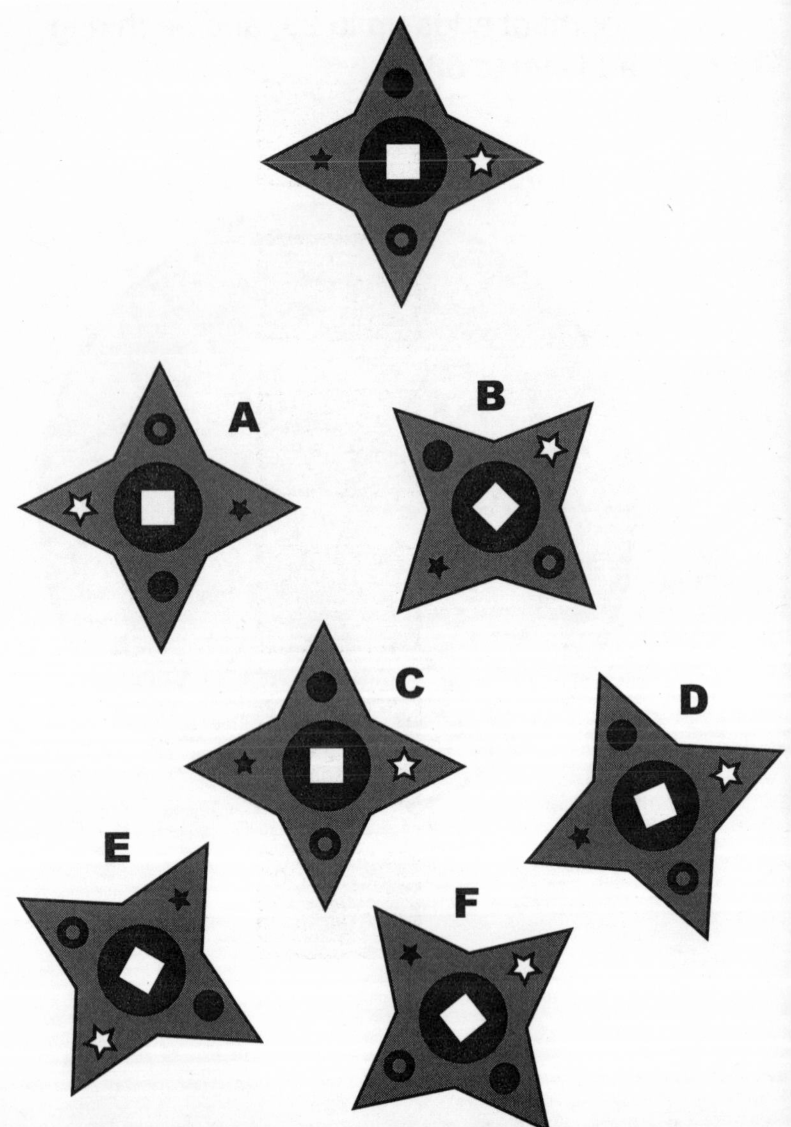

7

What is the missing number in this sequence?

11

17

?

14

8

8

Which letter is missing from this grid?

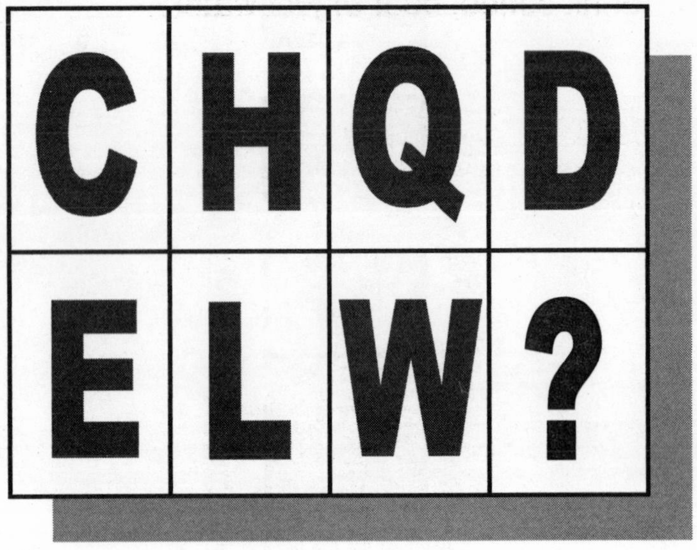

9

It's break time at Bradley's Coal Yard. Mr Bradley drinks tea, and Sue Smith, his secretary, drinks juice.

Does John Leech, the head coalman, drink coffee, beer or just water?

10

Fill in the missing shapes.

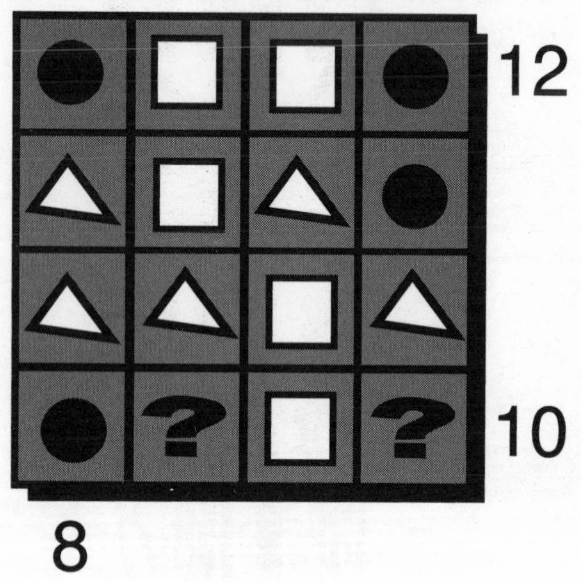

11

Which number should replace the question mark?

12

Can you find 10 differences between these two boxes?

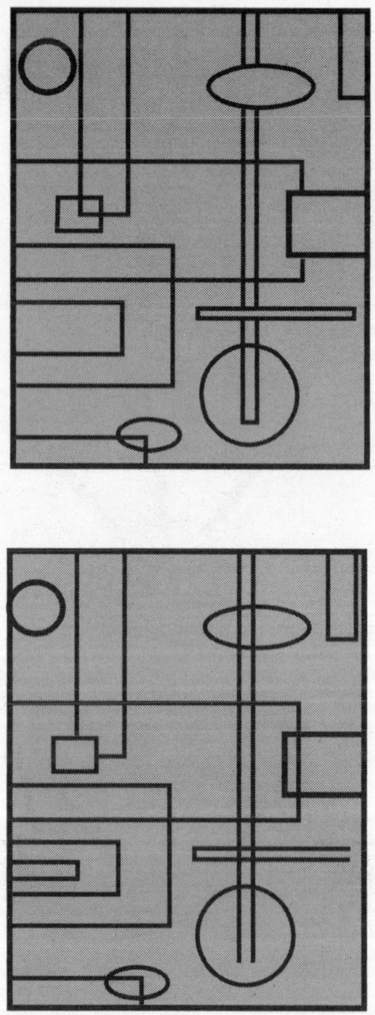

13

Can you work out the missing number?

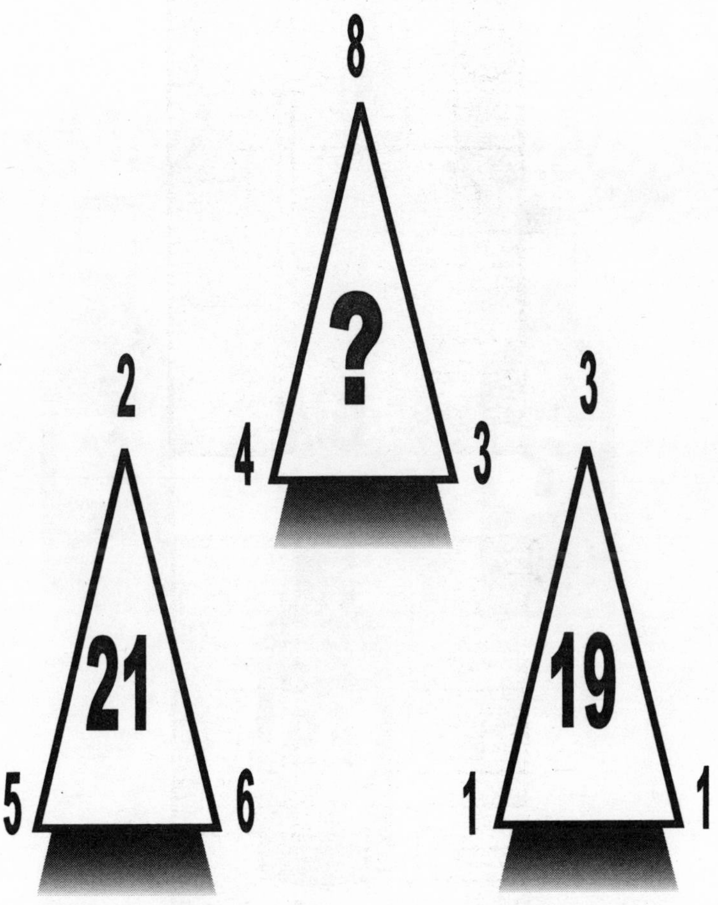

14

How much would you have to pay for the bottle of whiskey?

15

Martin says that there are 9 stops on the train journey from his home to Crewe, and 7 stops to Edinburgh.

How many does he reckon there are on the journey to Shrewsbury?

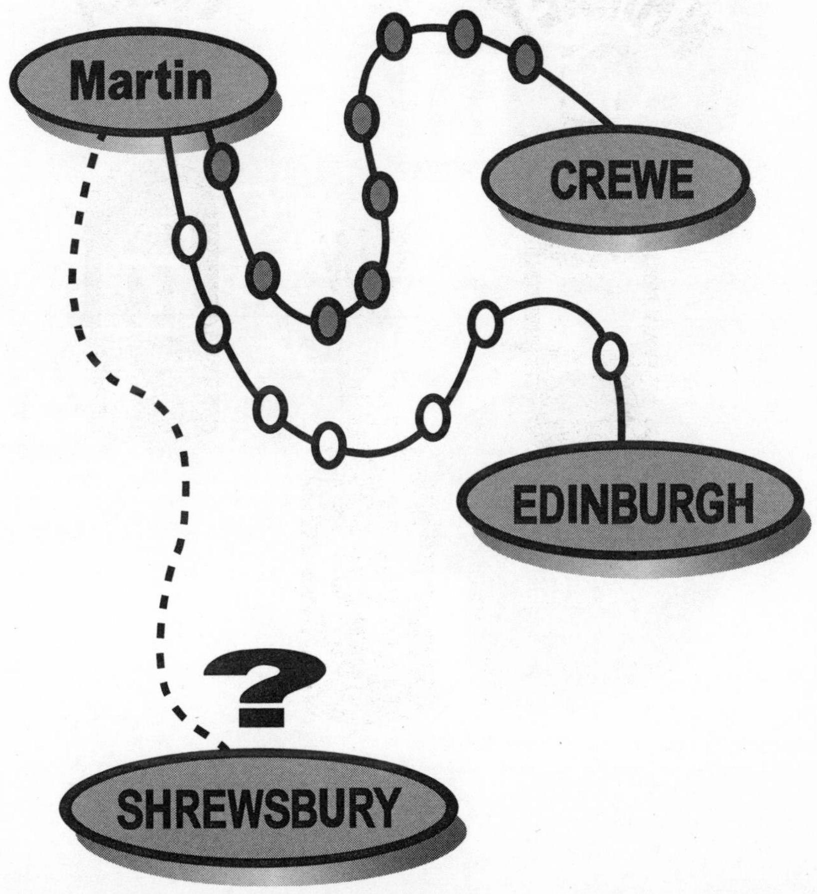

16

What is the missing number?

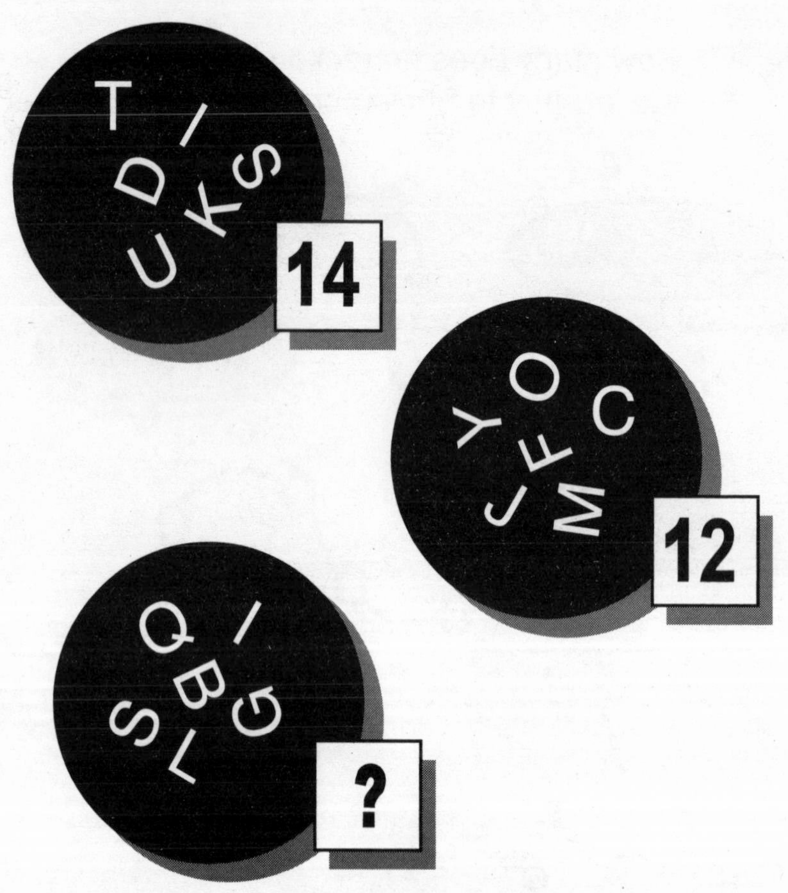

17

Which one is the odd one out?

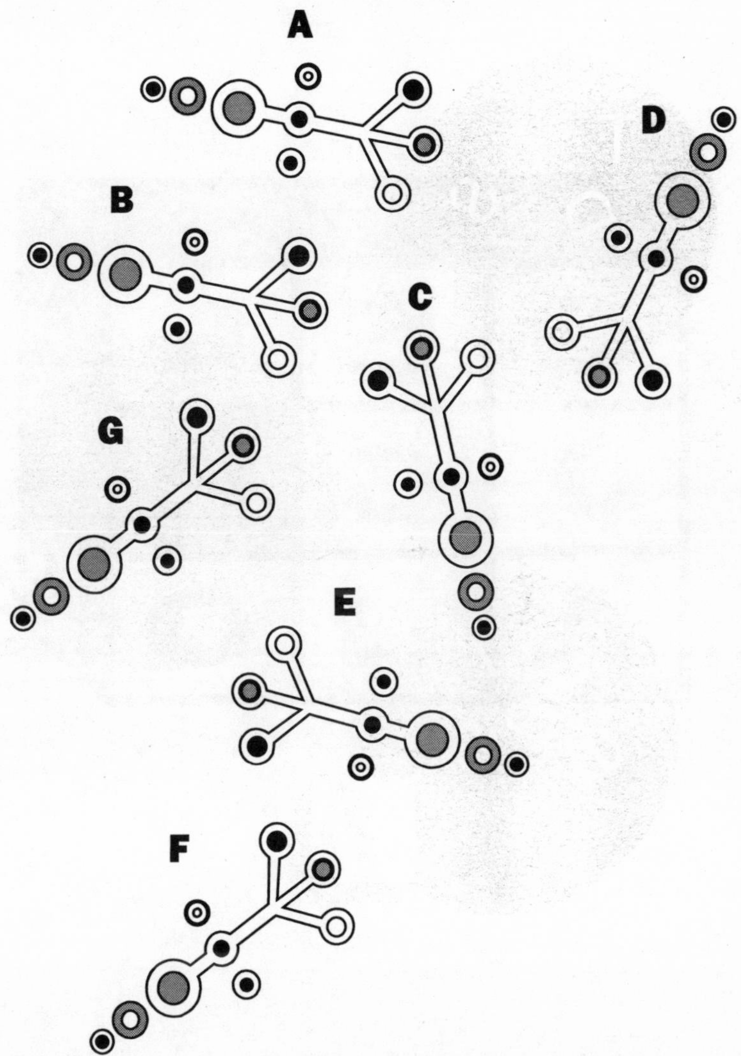

18

Which letter is missing?

19

What is the missing number?

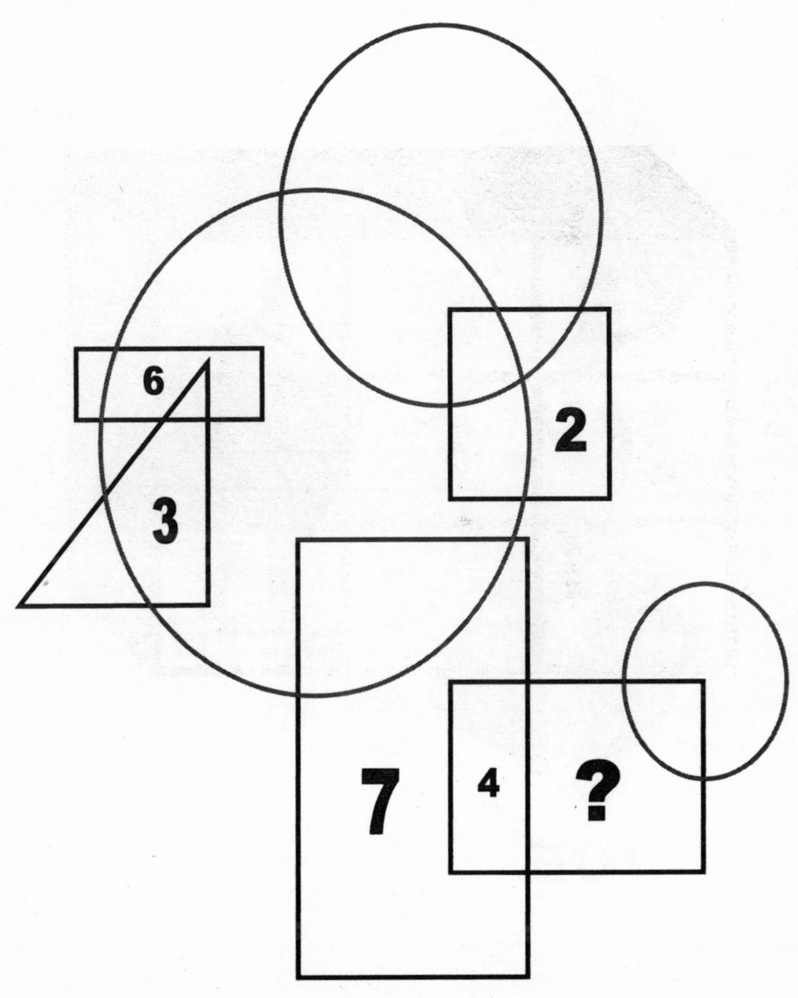

20

In a recent dice game, Sam threw a 2, Peter threw a 3, but what did Joe throw?

21

Below are five well-known film titles with the vowels missing and the other letters jumbled up.

What are they?

22

At what time does the afternoon train to Preston leave?

23

What is the missing number?

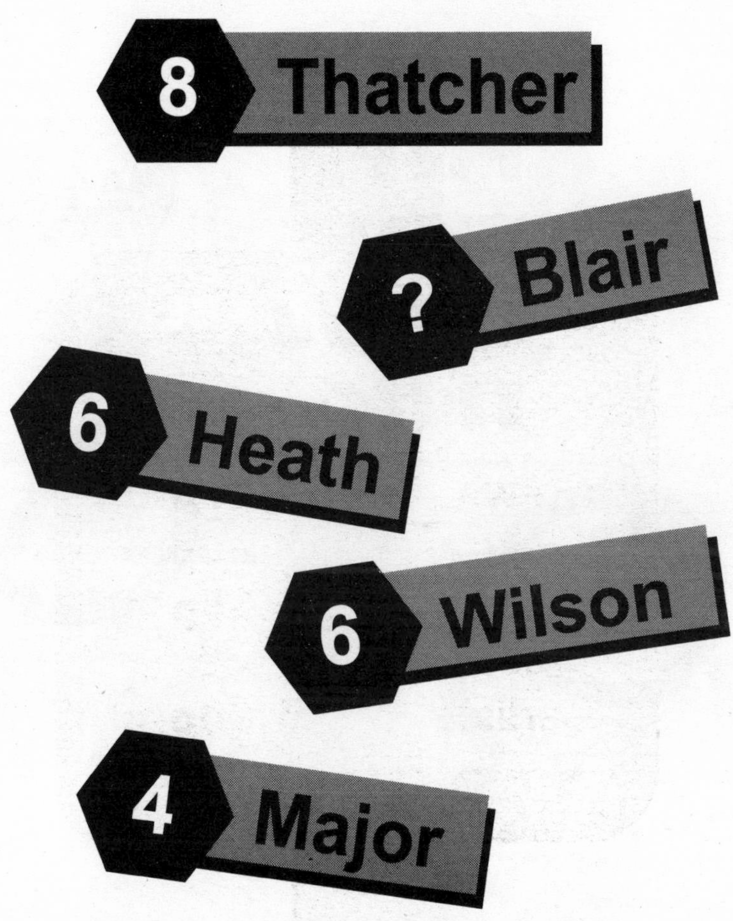

24

Which three letters will connect up this cable?

DUB
HIF
TOR
QSW
INK

25

Which number should replace the question mark?

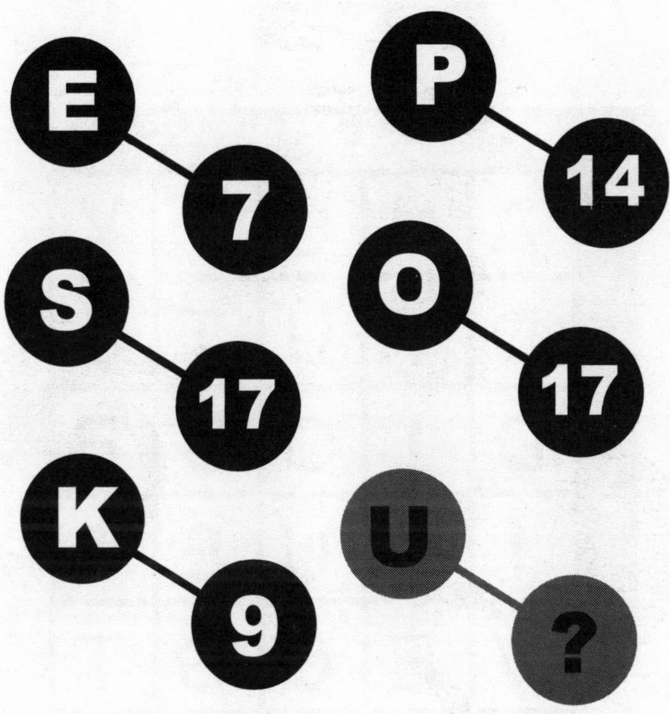

26

Move from square to square, including diagonally, to find the name of a popular BBC television programme.

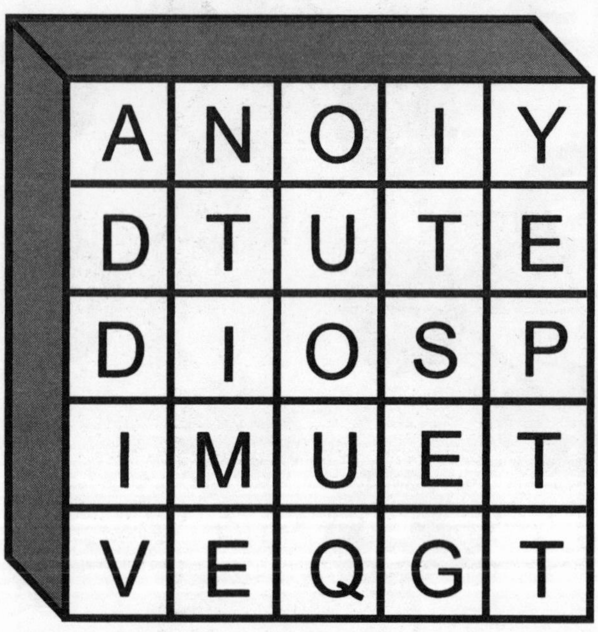

27

What number should you put in the bottom box?

28

Take one letter from each circle in order to spell out a nine-letter children's TV programme.

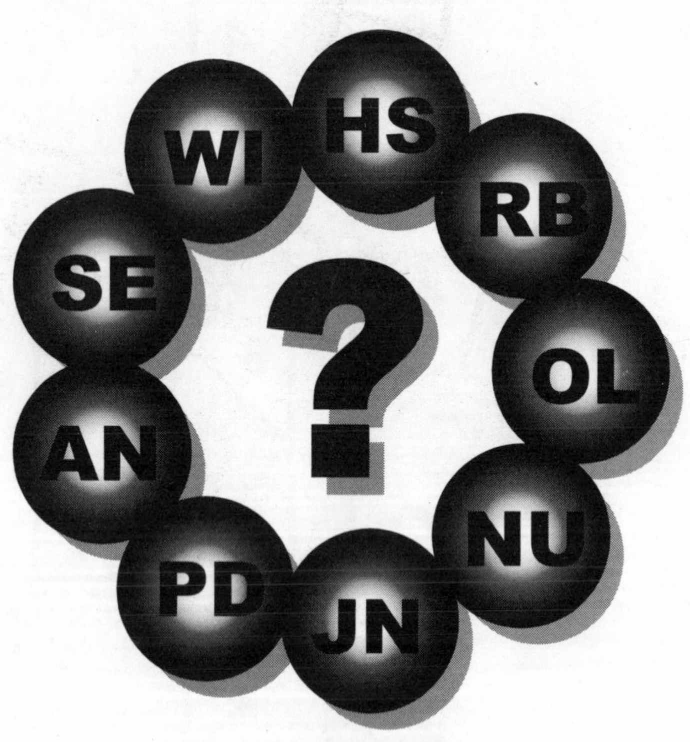

Fill in the missing number.

Which fruit should you add to the shopping list?

Strawberry, Grape, Blackcurrant or Apple?

31

What are the two missing numbers on this keypad?

32

Which letter should you add to this shape?

M I F X

33

Take the vowels from the circle and add them to the rectangles to make four words. Then decide which of the words is the odd one out.

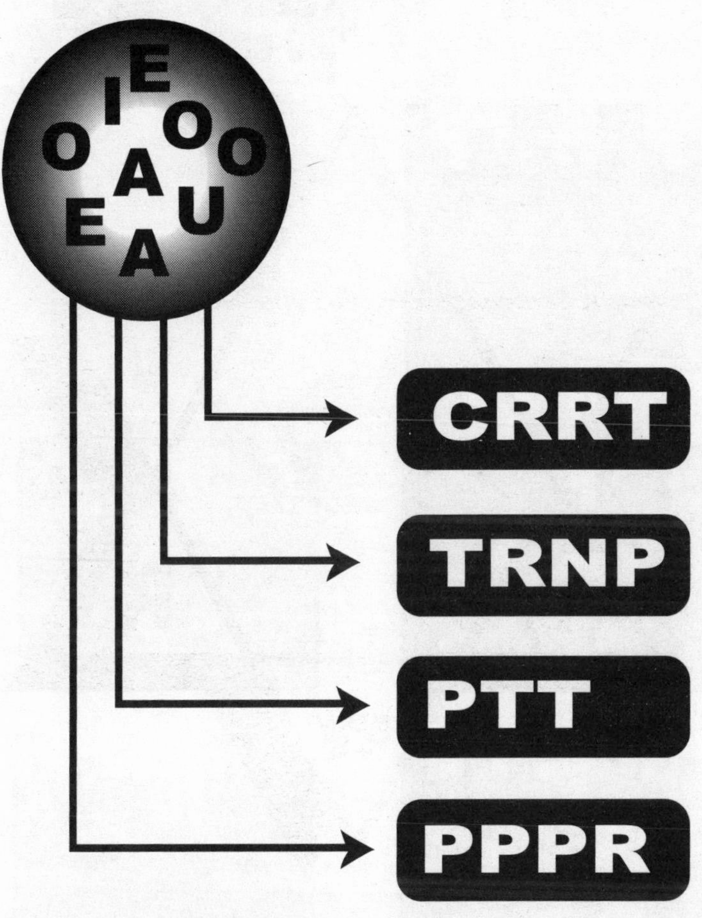

34

Which shape is the only one that completes this square?

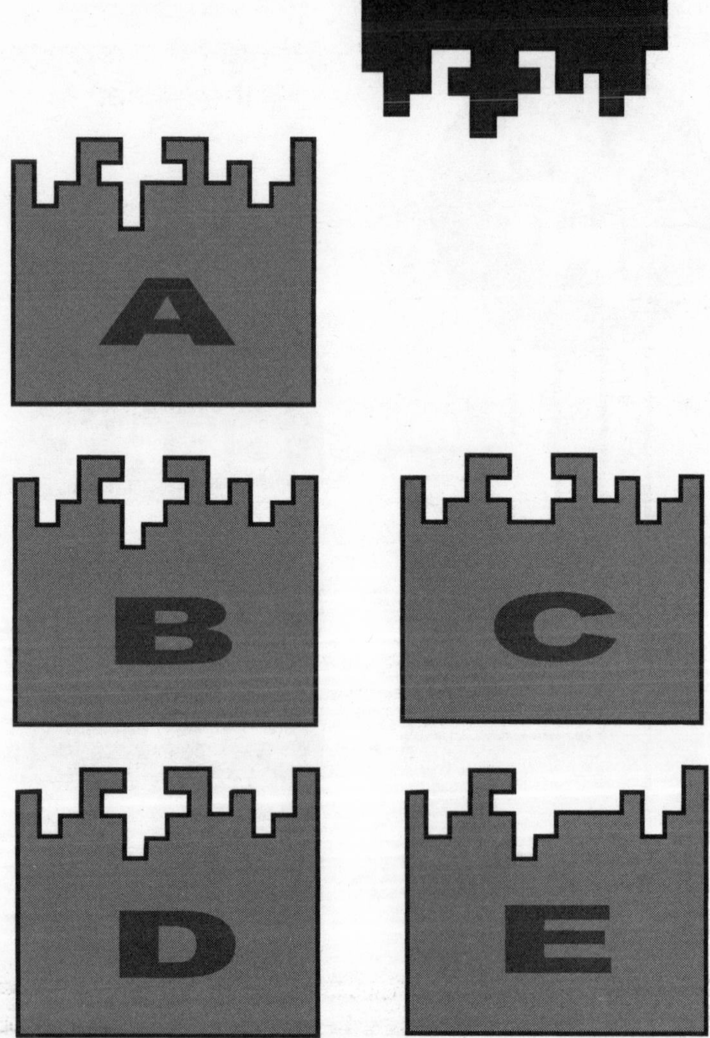

Work out the value of the question mark.

36

Which two letters are missing?

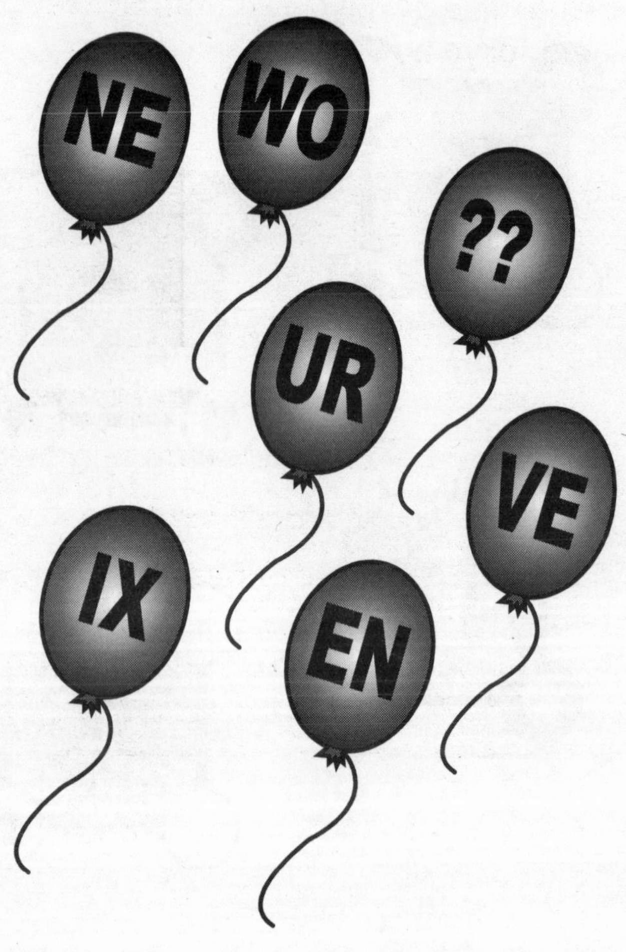

37

Here are some arrival times of flights to Heathrow airport.

What time do the flights from Sydney and Tokyo arrive?

ARRIVALS

SYDNEY	-- --
MOSCOW	10.08
BRUSSELS	14.10
TOKYO	-- --
TORONTO	11.10

38

Find the missing number.

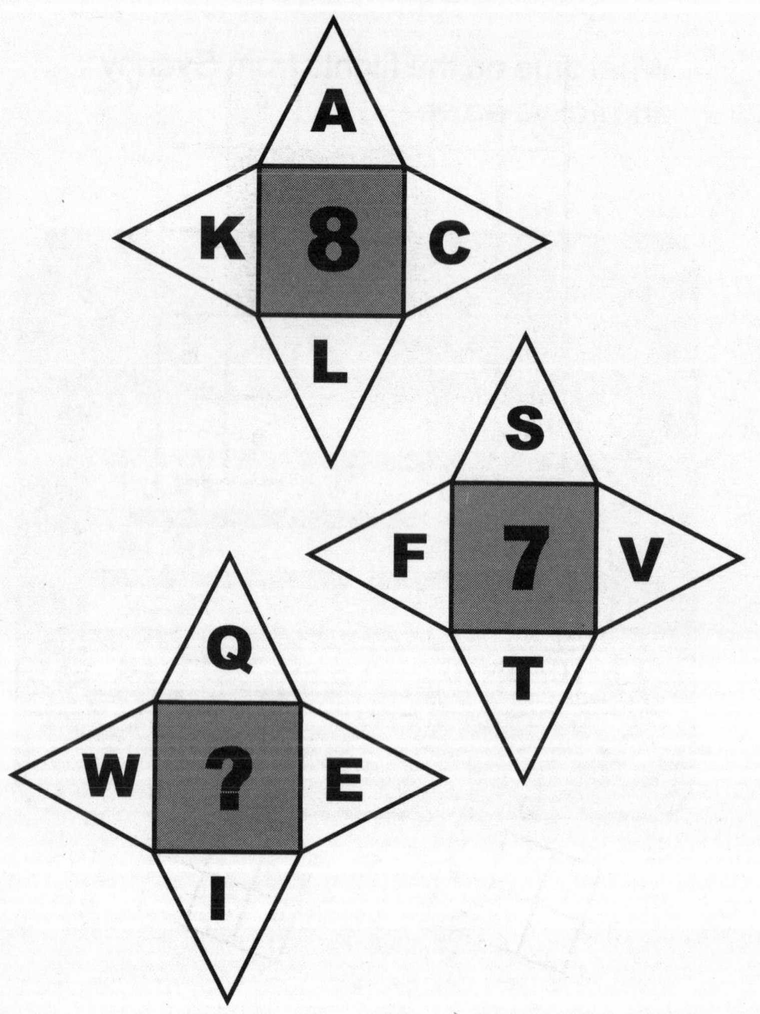

39

Replace the correct piece.

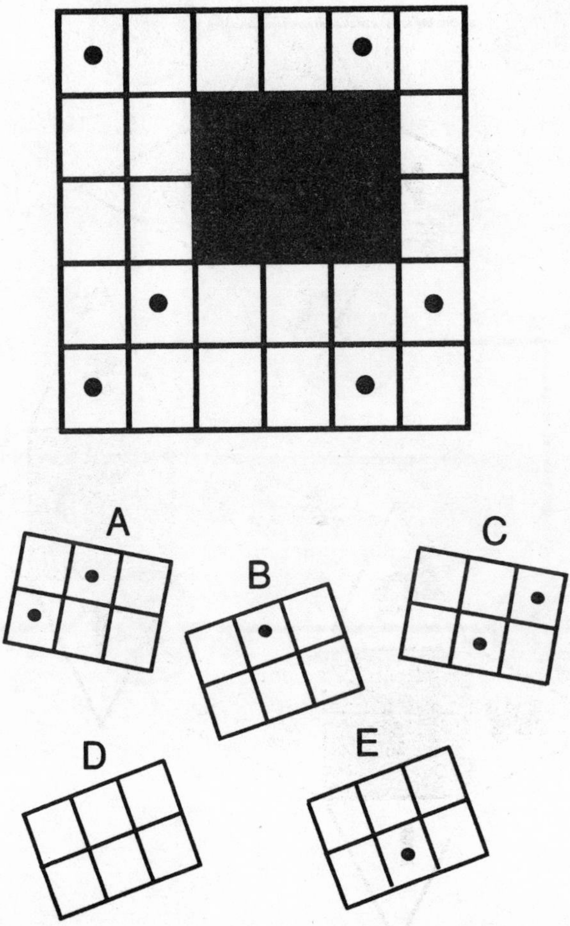

Which letter comes next?

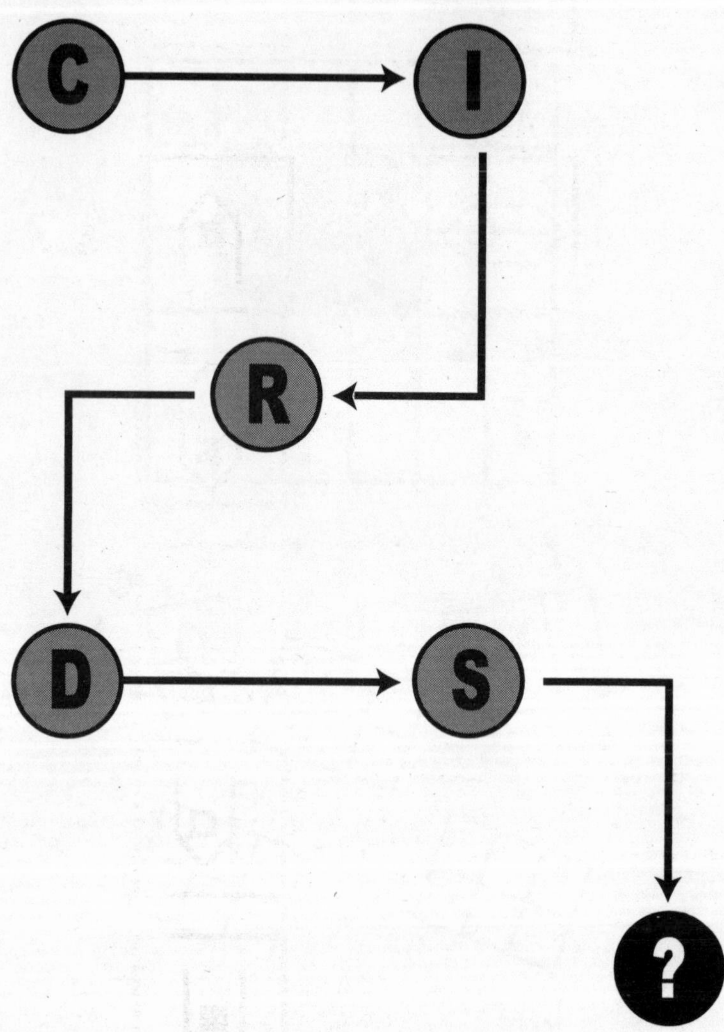

41

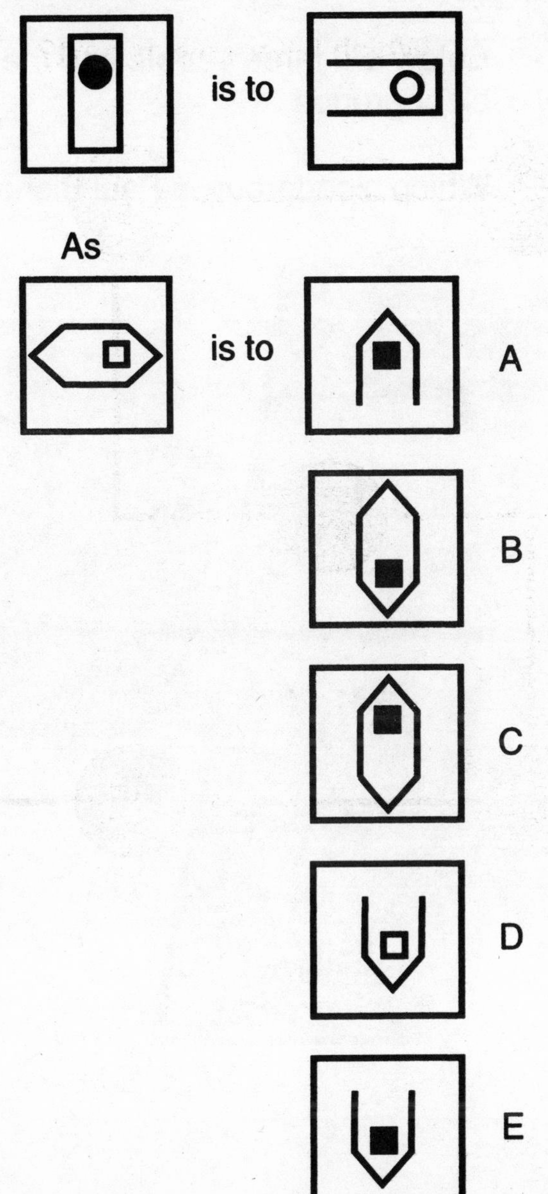

42

Below are three people and their bloodgroups.

Which bloodgroup is Paul Bishop?

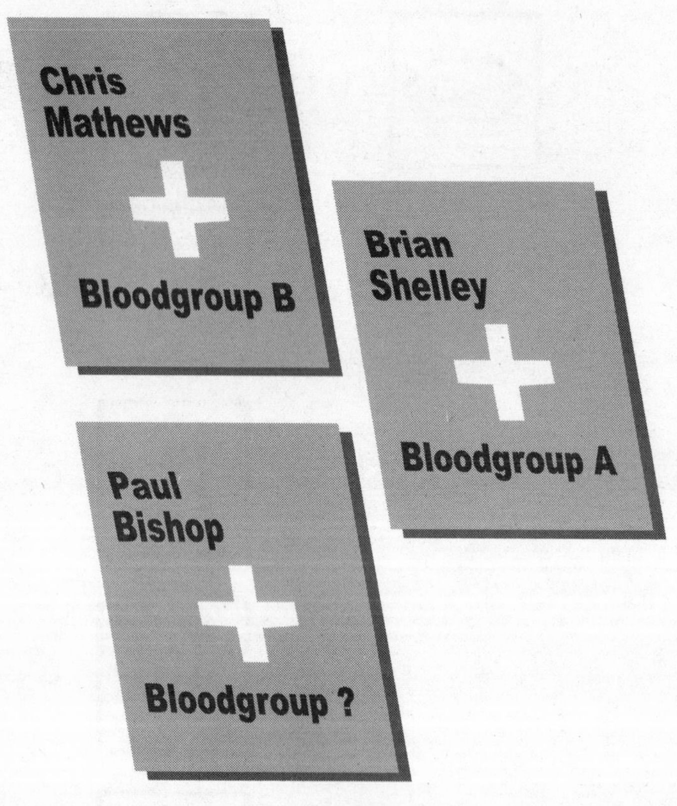

43

What number should accompany the bottom row of balls?

44

Merged together in this grid are the names of two countries.

What are they?

45

Which is the odd one out?

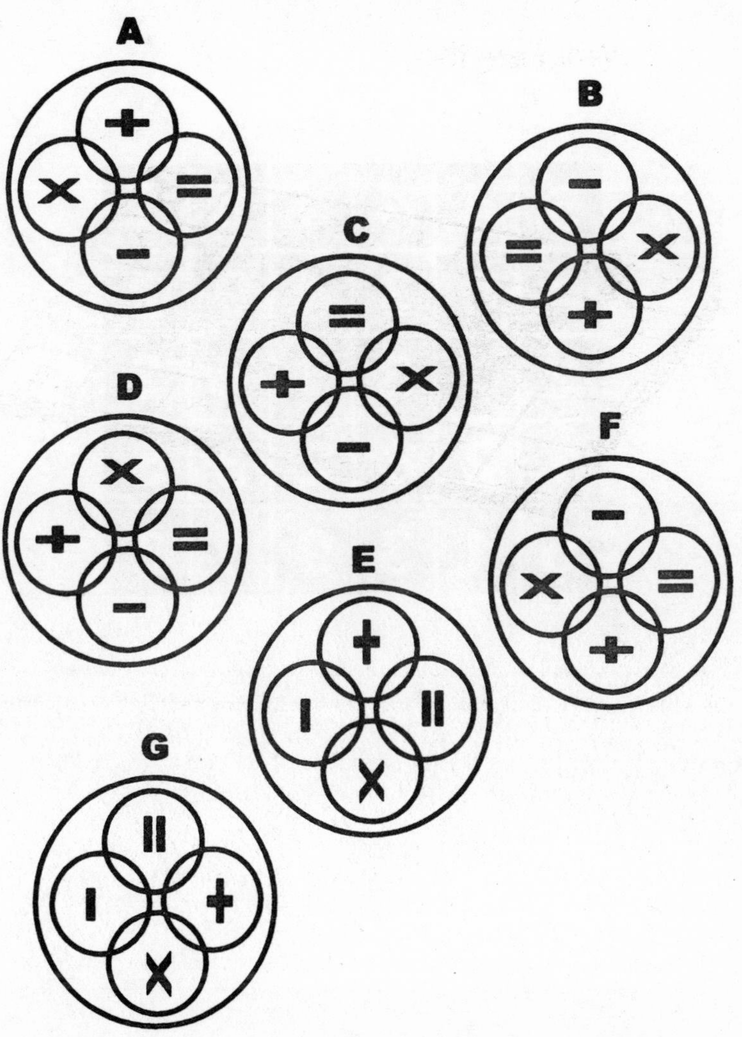

Work out the missing number.

5	4	4	1	6	1
4	6	3	4	9	2
2	7	3	1	4	2
1	2	8	2	3	5
6	1	3	9	?	3

Below are the finishers in the 3.15 at Uttoxeter.

Did *Beeches Boy* come in fourth, fifth or sixth?

1. TWIST 45

2. FADHEL

3. MISS TANGO

The alphabet below is incomplete.

Rearrange the missing letters into the name of a town in the UK.

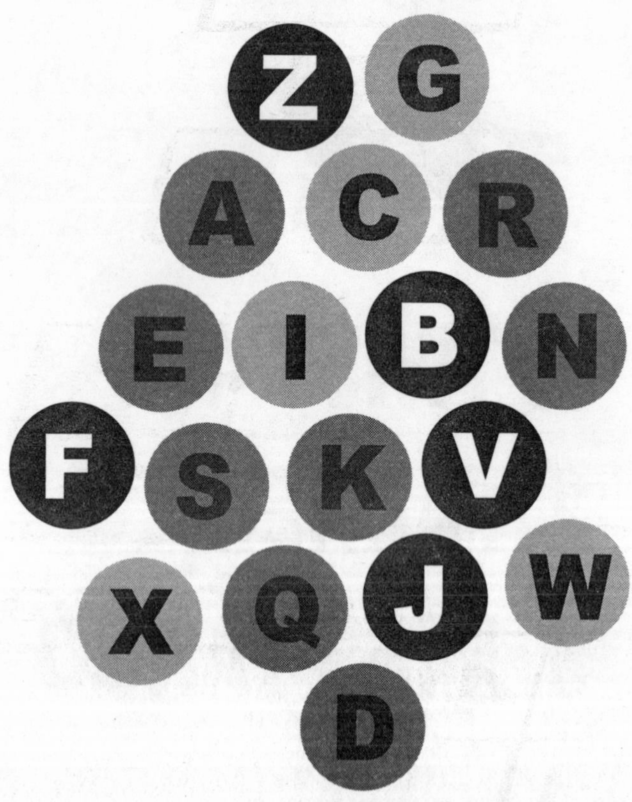

49

Work out the missing number.

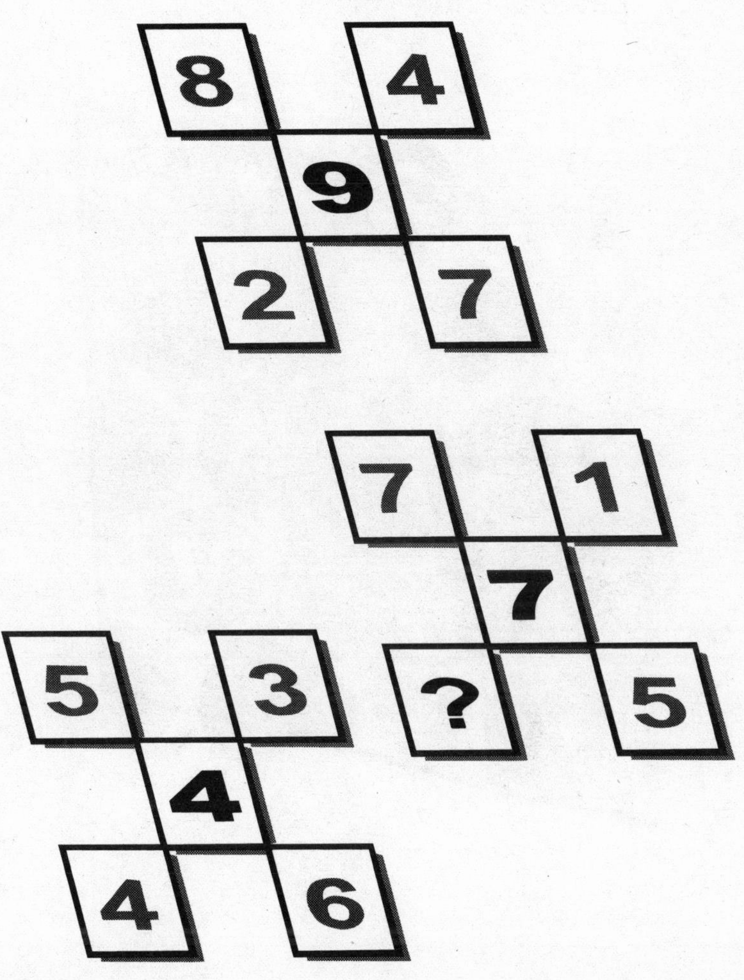

50

If **WIFX**
is FROG, what does this message say?

51

Work out the missing number.

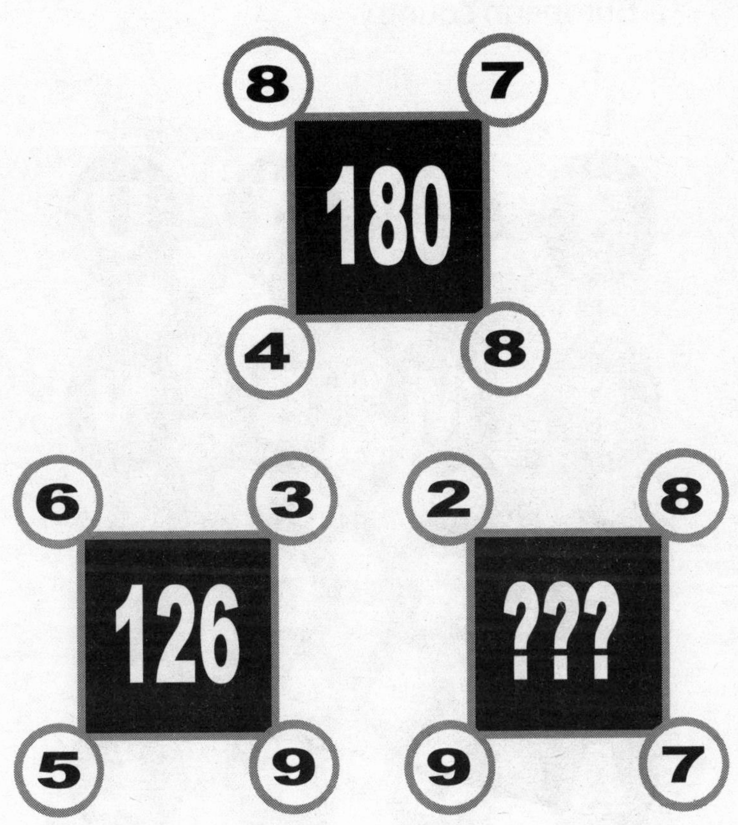

Join the letters together using straight lines, including diagonally, and without crossing over a line, to find the name of a European country.

53

Work out the missing number.

11	19	21	?

How tall is the Willow tree?

55

Which number should replace the question mark?

Below are the recent rainfall figures.

How many centimetres fell in Devon?

57

You find a bundle of £10 notes numbered consecutively from 751422 to 758321.

How much money is in the bundle?

A. £69,060
B. £69,000
C. £68,450
D. £68,970
E. £69,100

58

What number should you put in column 4?

59

Unravel the names of these film actors, then decide who is the odd one out.

CONCEALASIGH
MANIACILEECH
SANDIFHORROR
WITHMILLS
SWIRLLIECUB

60

Move from square to square, including diagonally, to find the name of a London landmark.

61

What is the missing number?

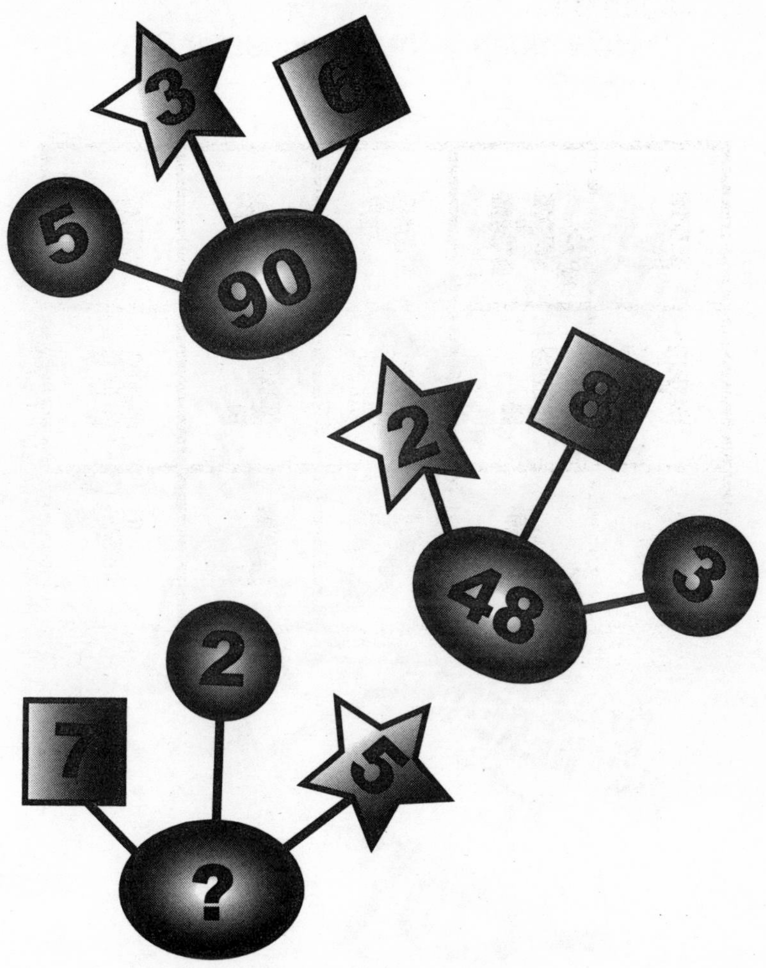

62

The cost of some replica football shirts are shown below.

How much is the Manchester City shirt?

63

Which number is missing from this sequence?

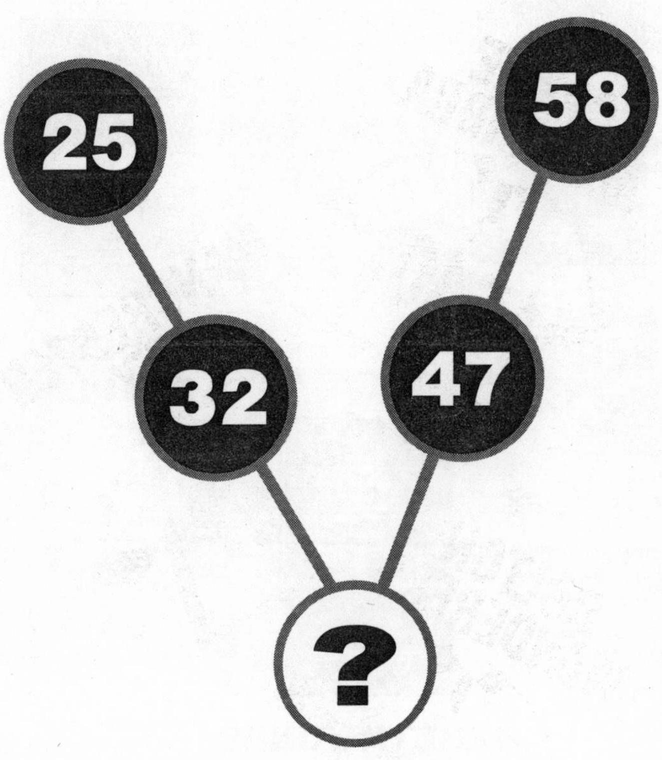

64

What is Robert Chaplin's new passport number?

SARAH KENNEDY
No: 1275

ROBERT CHAPLIN
No: ?

GARETH JONES
No: 1156

65

Which letter is missing from the bottom circle?

Hidden in this grid you can find: Boat, Truck, Donkey, Scooter and Hovercraft.

Use the remaining letters to construct another method of transport.

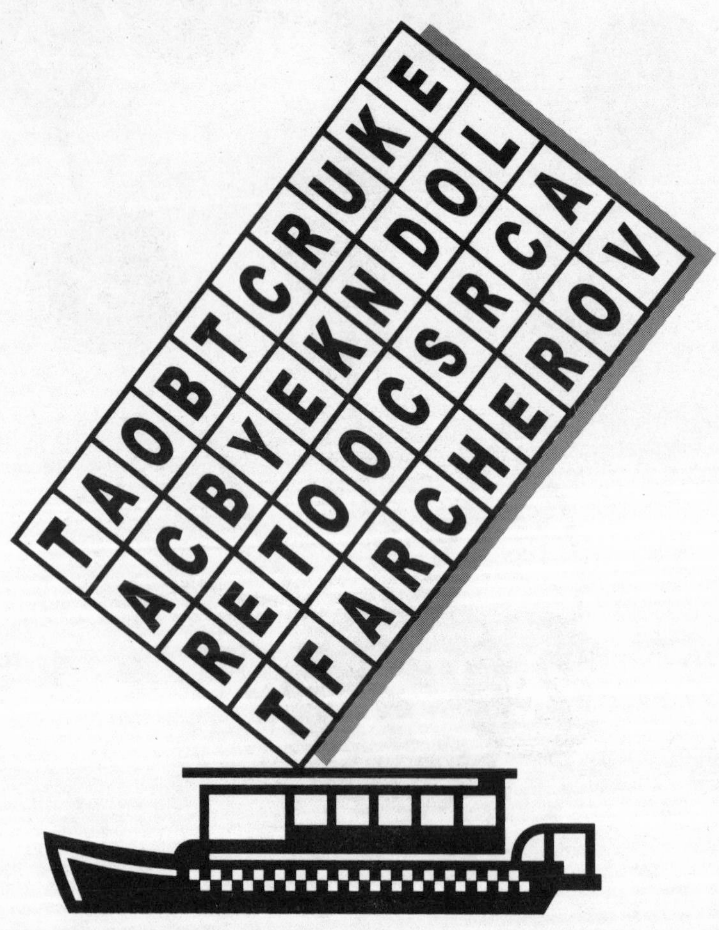

67

Which number comes next in this sequence?

68

What does this code message say?

GUR CBFG NEEVIRF NG
FRIRA GUVEGL N.Z.

69

Which pattern is a mirror image of this one?

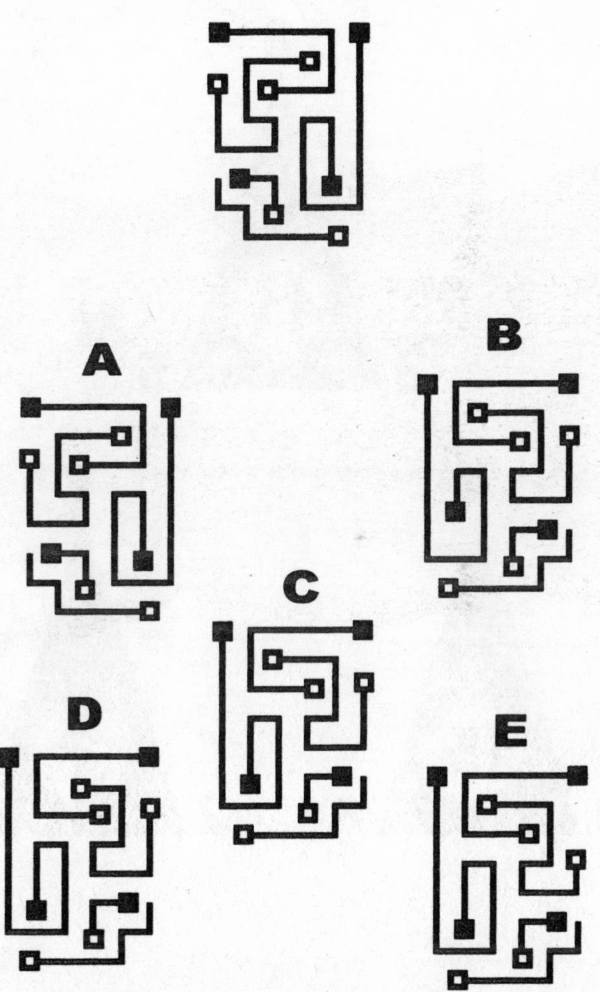

Find the missing number.

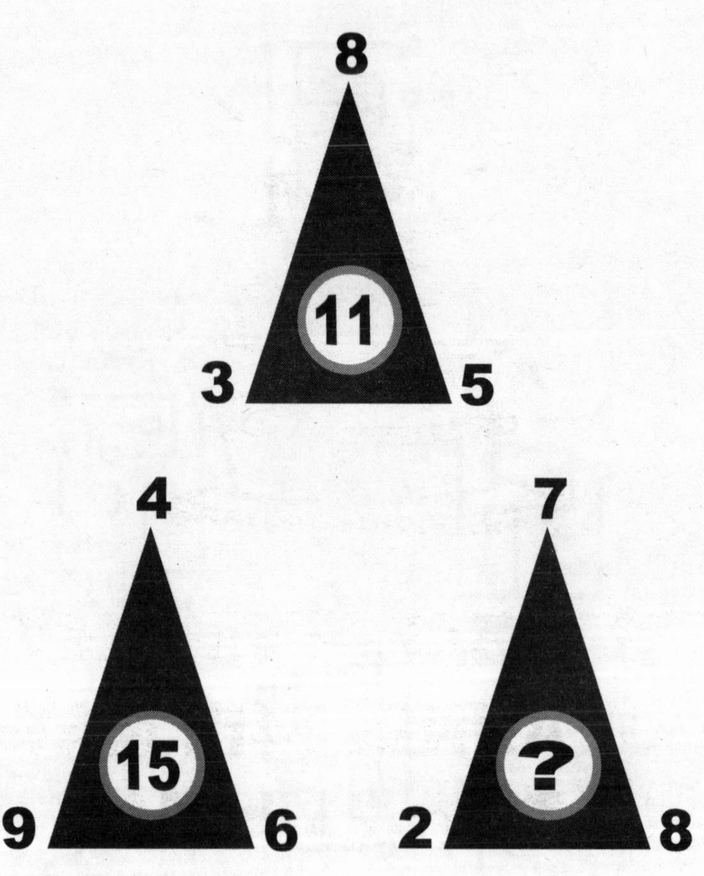

71

Four friends are getting married in May this year. What date is Rebecca's wedding?

BARBARA: 1st MAY
JOANNE: 14th MAY
CATHY: 25th MAY
REBECCA: ??

72

Which spiral is missing from this sequence?

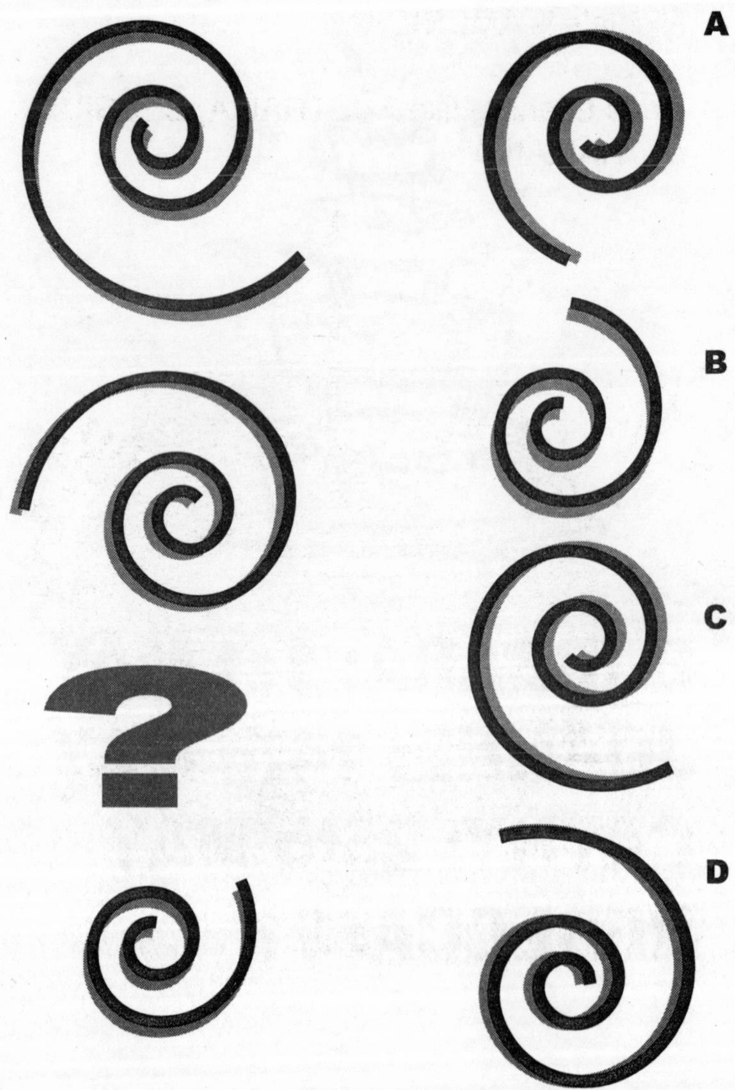

73

Julie's favourite country is FRANCE, David's favourite is HOLLAND, and Nicola's is AMERICA.

Does Graham like AUSTRALIA, BELGIUM or THAILAND?

If the van is worth 4, the car 2, and the bike 1, what is the value of the question mark?

75

Pick out the mirror image of the square below.

A

B

C

D

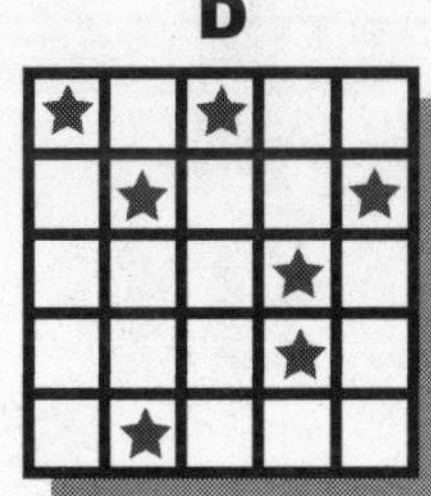

E

What is the missing number?

77

Unravel the names of these UK places.

STHUTOPROM

REVLOWPHANTOM

RINGDUBHE

NOTMANIGHT

Which satellite will connect up these two Communication Centres?

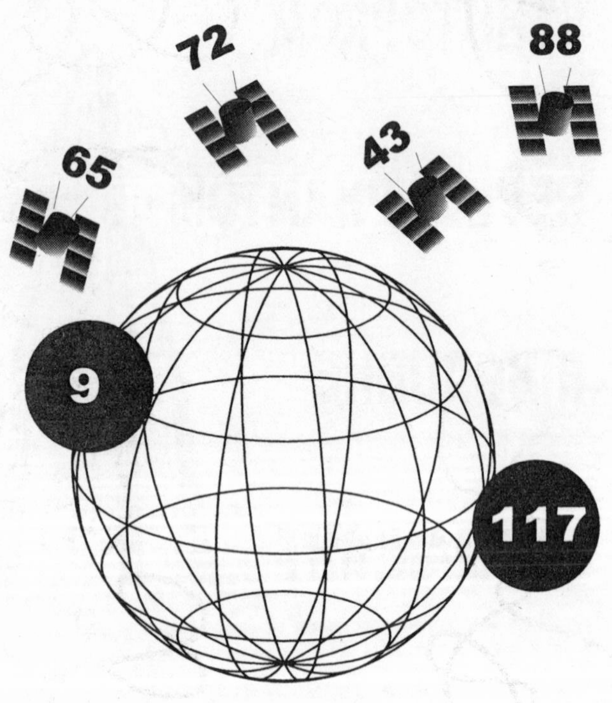

Which shape replaces the question mark?

80

Each of these places in the USA has a certain number of postal districts.

How many are there in Austin?

81

The people below have recently been allocated new e-mail addresses.

Can you complete Gillian's?

Dave Williams: dave@19131.co.uk
Susan Tovey: susan@25522.co.uk

Gillian Peacock: gillian@ **?** .co.uk

Which sequence of stepping stones (1 from each row) should you use to get from A to B?

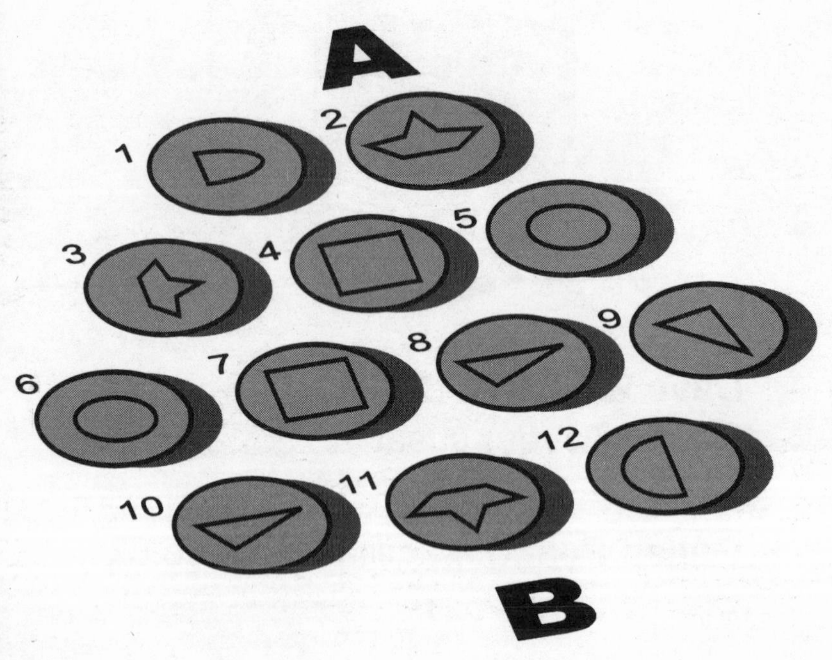

83

What should the time be on the last clock?

84

You arrive at a road junction. You know from your map that it is 16 miles to Shrewsbury, 12 miles to Nantwich and 6 miles to Crewe.

How far is it to Chester?

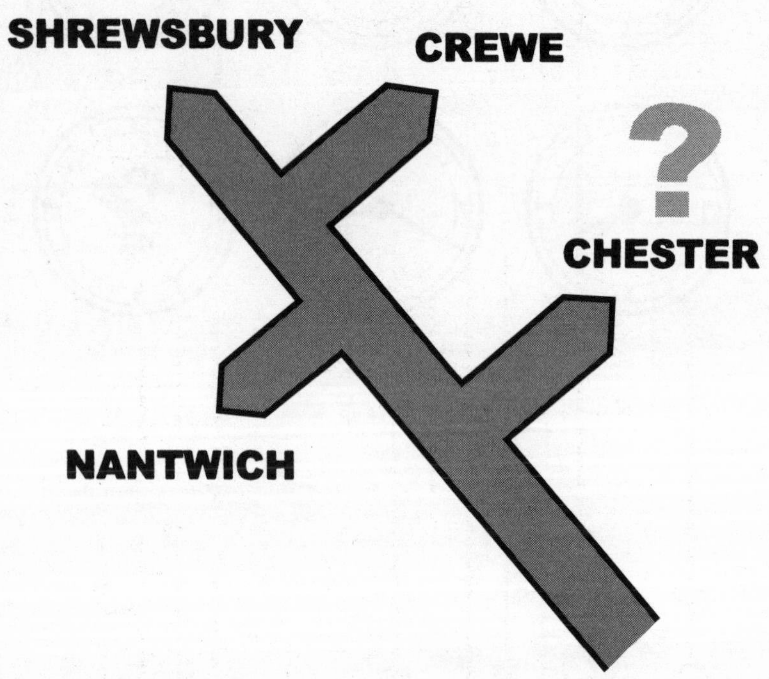

85

Which piece connects this grid back together?

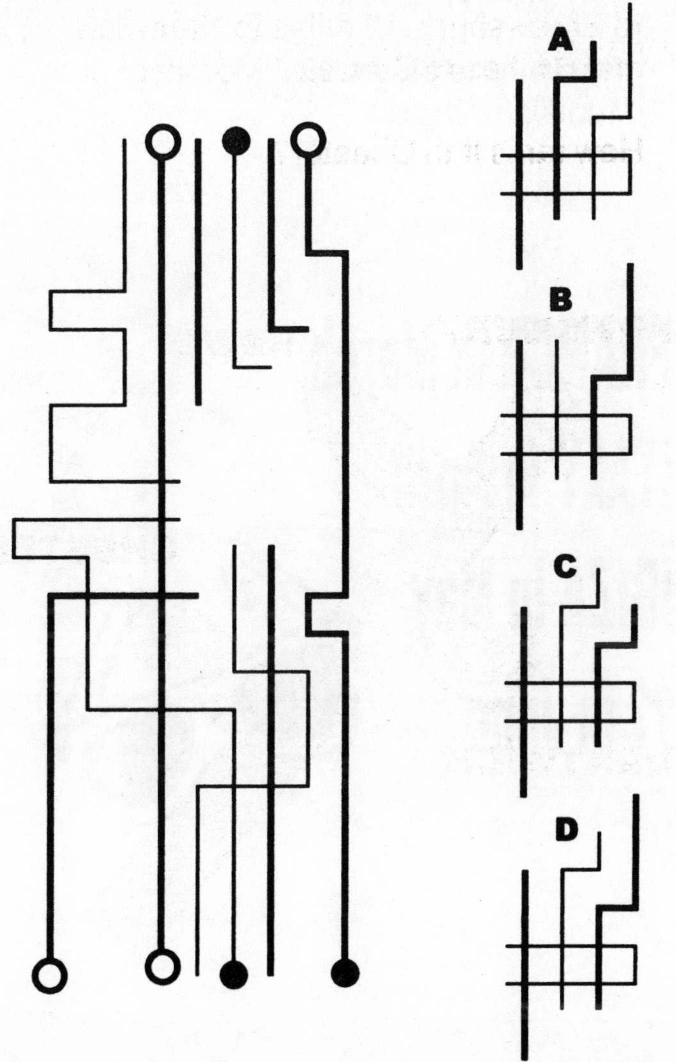

Scott loves holidays. This year he's visited the places below.

But in June did he visit Morocco, Tunisia or Iran?

FRANCE in March

ITALY in April

IBIZA in May

?? in June

87

Fill in the missing number to complete the telephone number below.

20 1 2 12 ?

88

A number of decorators were interviewed to discover their favourite hobbies.

How many liked jogging?

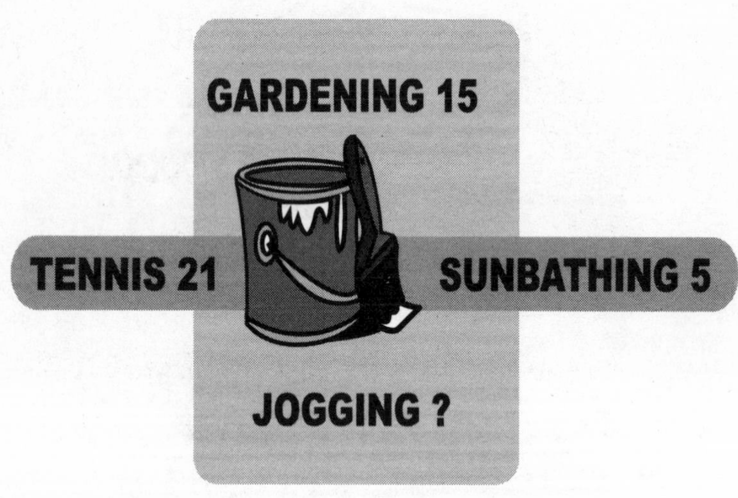

Does the flight to Tokyo make a stopover in Rangoon, Bombay or Tehran?

HONG KONG stopover in FRANKFURT

JAKARTA stopover in HYDERABAD

MEXICO CITY stopover in KINGSTON

Which shape is the mirror image of the one below?

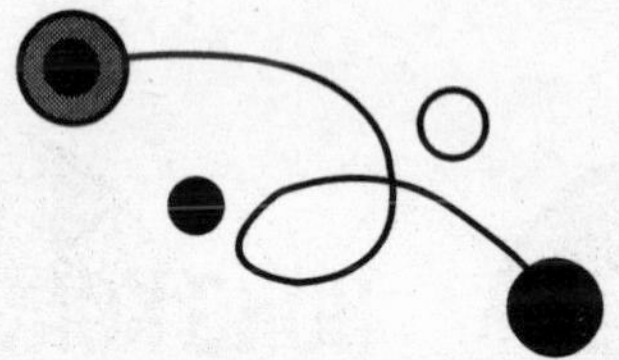

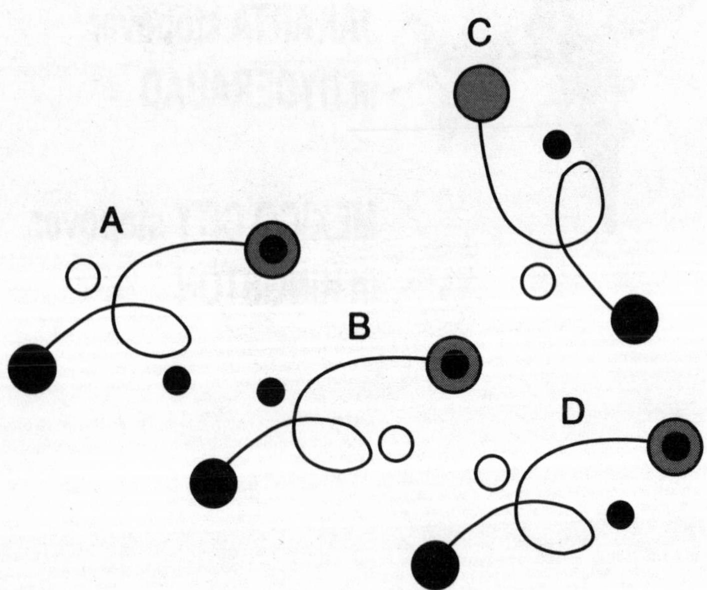

91

What is the score on target C?

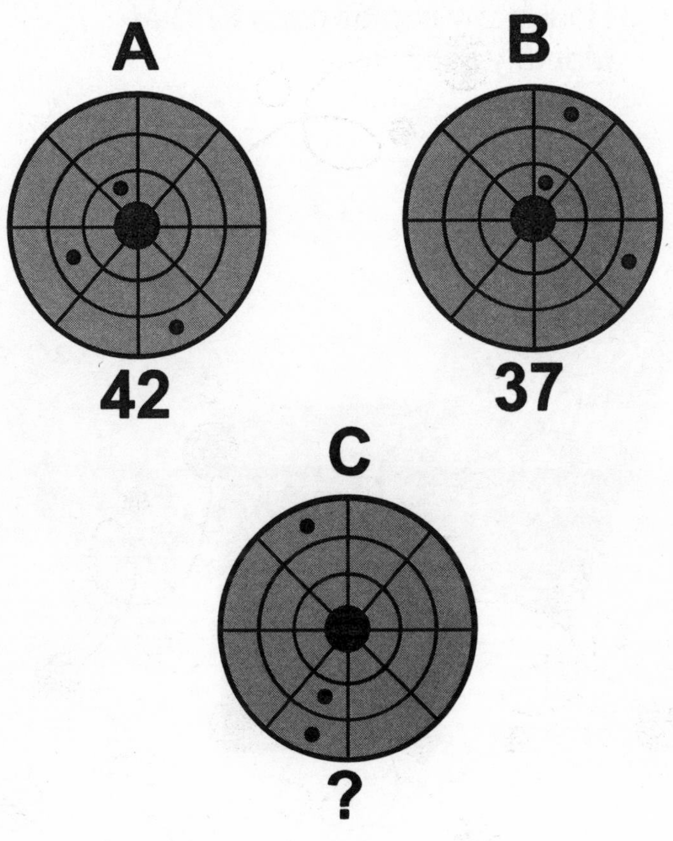

?

92

Here are some magazines and their circulation figures.

How many copies does Cricket Monthly sell?

93

What number goes in the last shape?

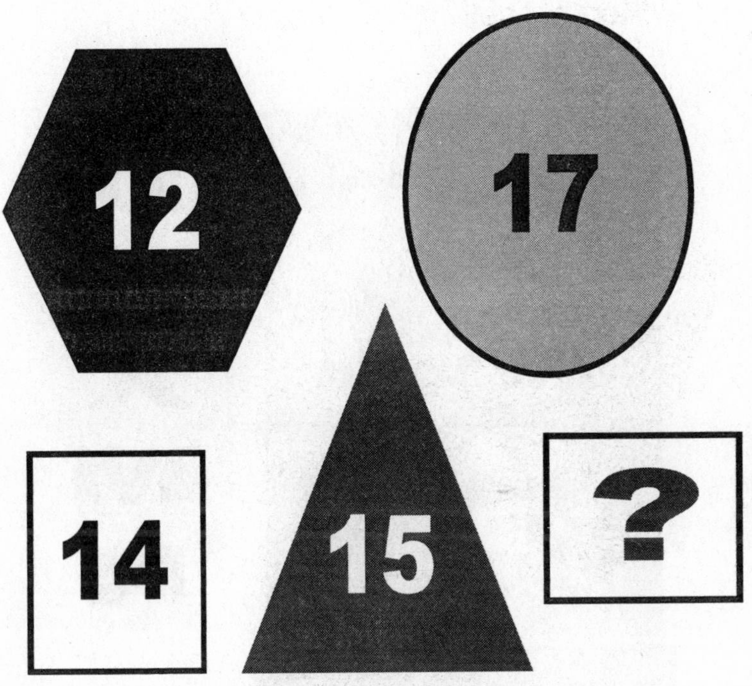

94

Add the correct letter to open the safe.

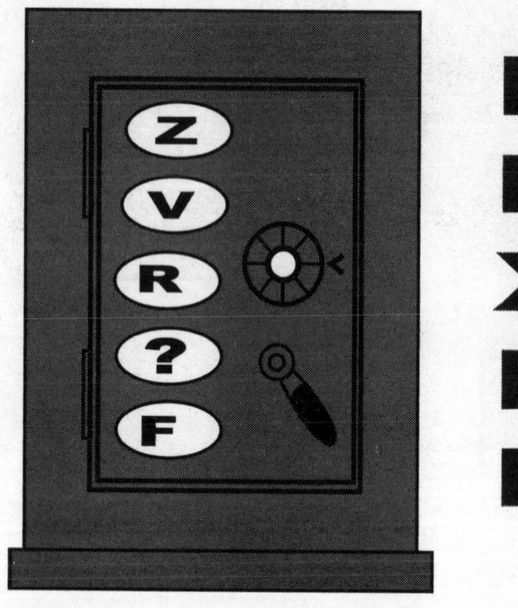

D
L
X
M
N

95

How many miles is it to Newbury?

Take one letter from each circle to spell out the name of a popular breed of dog.

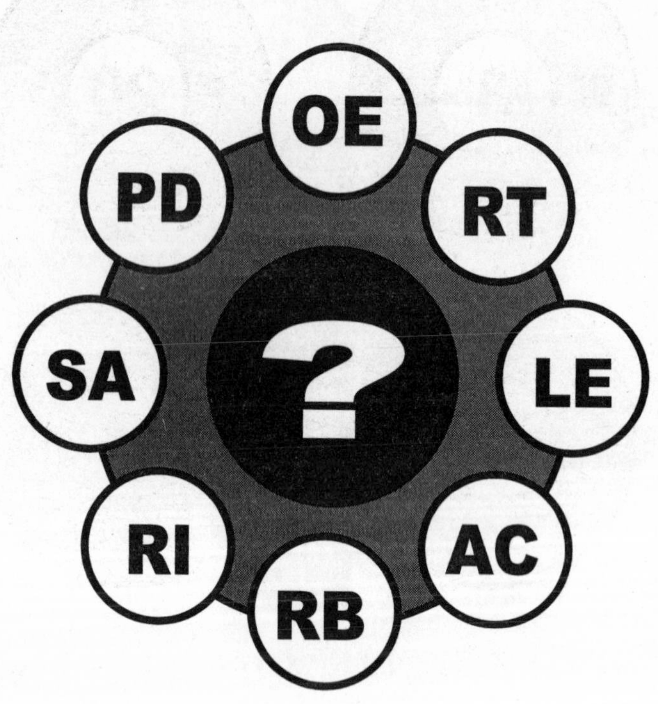

What is the missing number?

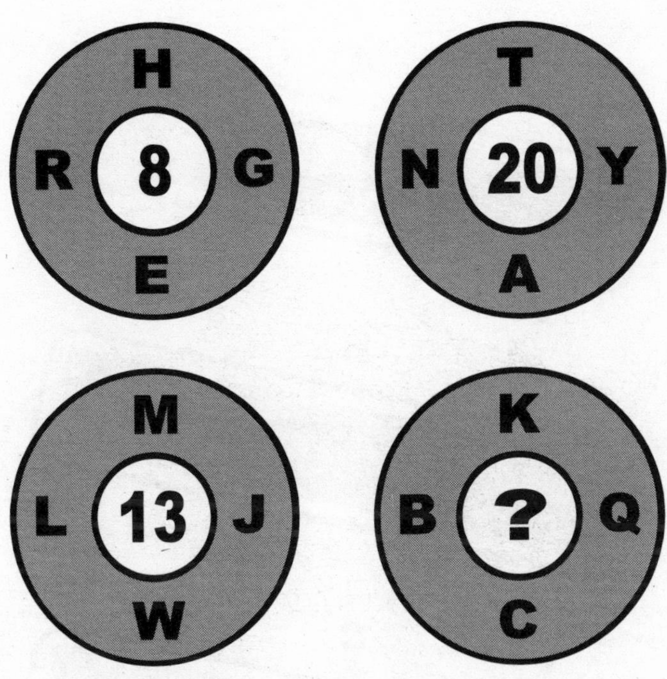

Which of these classic number plates is incorrect?

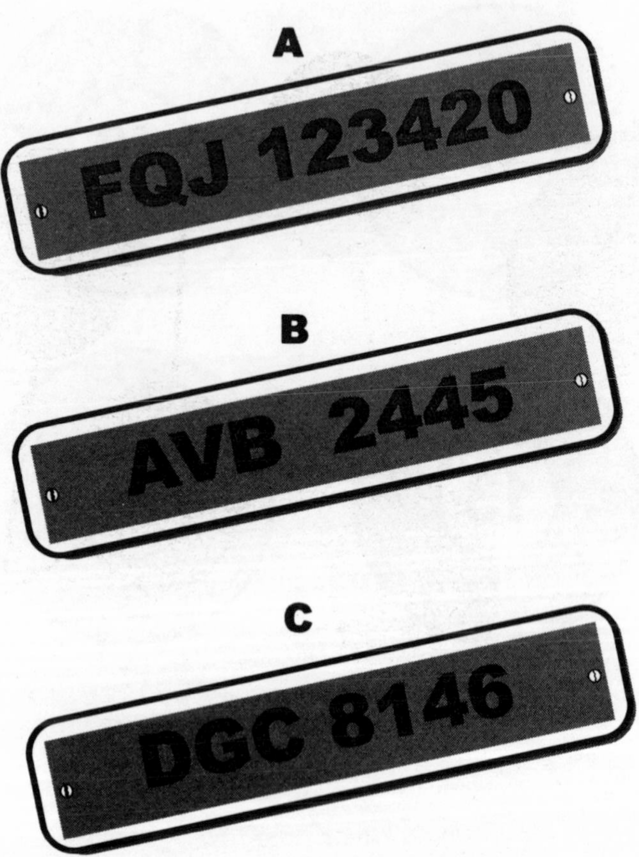

99

Work out the missing number.

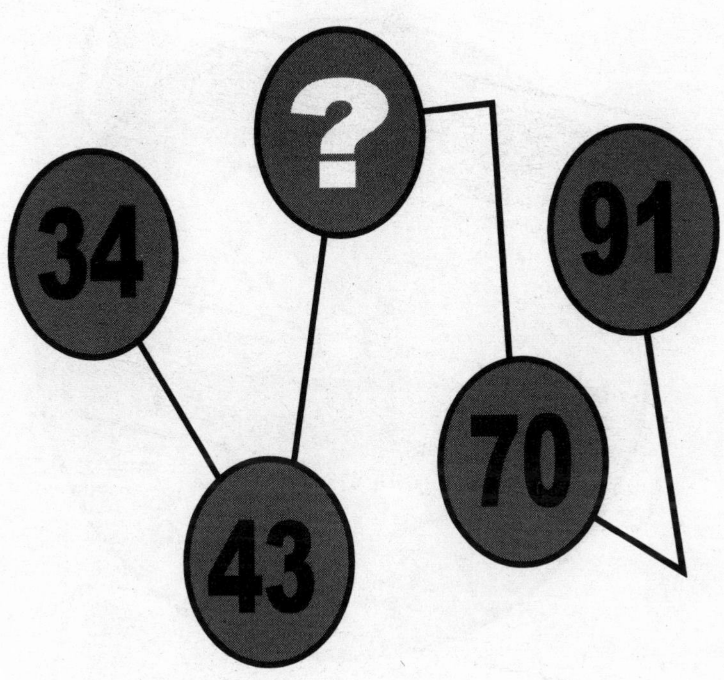

100

Find the two missing numbers.

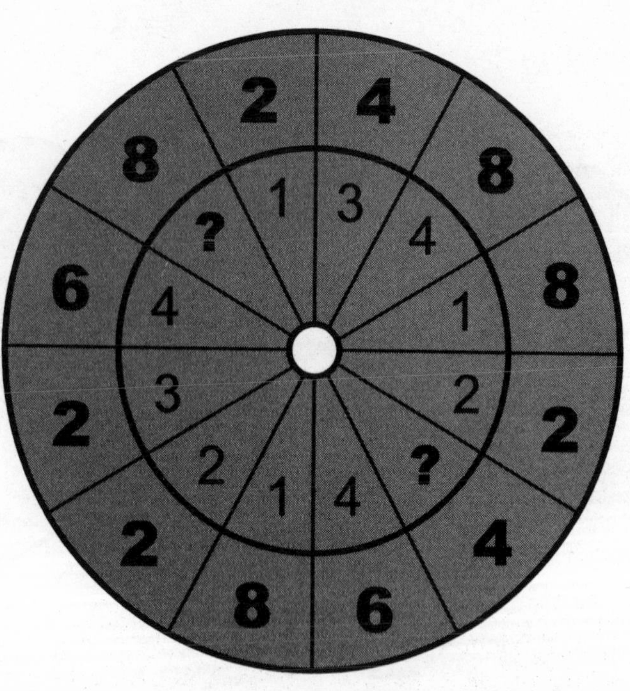

Solutions

1 6. 368 divided by 16 equals 23.

2 The missing letter is A. Pawpaw, Peach, Apple and Orange.

3 Brussels.

4 30. The number of letters in the first word of the title, multiplied by ten.

5 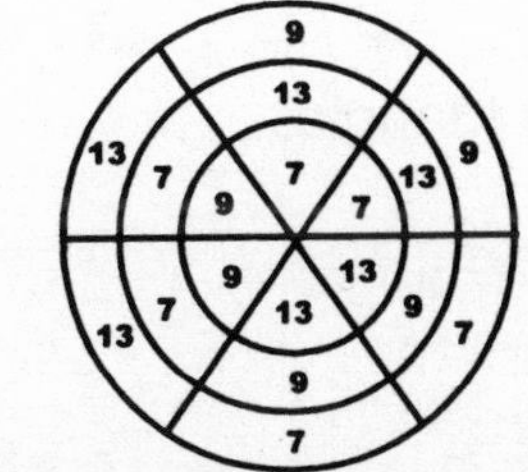

6 F.

7 20. Starting with number 5 add 3 each time to the bottom of the line, then the top: 8, 11, 14, 17 and 20.

8 L. C is the first segment. Move two places in the alphabet to the second square, three places to the third, four to the fourth, and so on through to the eighth segment.

9 Coffee. The vowels in the name are the same as in the preferred drink.

10 △ = 3
□ = 5
● = 1 A circle and a triangle.

11 62. The first two numbers are actually together, so 66 minus 4 equals 62.

12 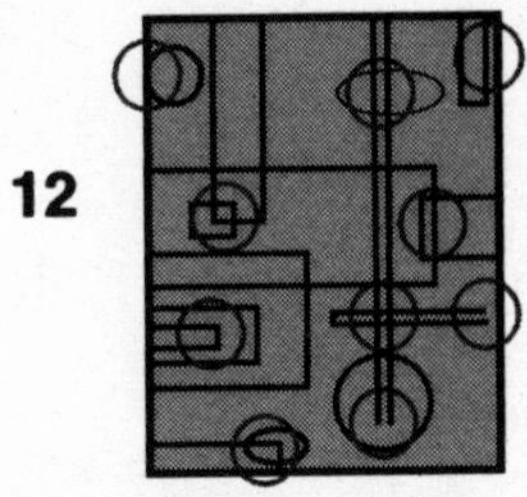

13 19. Take the top number from each triangle: $2 \times 8 = 16 + 3 = 19$.

14 £19. The alphanumeric value of the middle letter of the name.

15 5. The number of letters between the first letter in Martin and the first letter of the destination.

16 11. Add together the alphanumeric values of all the letters in the circle, then divide by 6, the number of letters in the circle.

17 C.

18 M. The alphanumeric values of J + C = M.

19 3. The number of straight lines in the shape, minus the number of curved lines that cross it.

20 1. The number of letters in the name, minus the number of vowels.

21 A Clockwork Orange, Gone with the Wind, Jurassic Park, Jaws and Star Wars.

22 3.30pm. Half the number of letters in the destination.

23 4. Each number corresponds to the number of letters in each of these PM's Christian names.

24 TOR. Put between S and M they spell the word STORM. The others don't spell any word.

25 23. Vowels: alphanumeric value plus 2; Consonants: alphanumeric value minus 2.

26

	N	O	I	
	T		T	
	I		S	
	M	U	E	
	E	Q		

27 16. Add together the bottom right number from each box.

28 Newsround.

29 4. Add all of the numbers together to make 57.

30 Blackcurrant. All of the items on the list contain 3 vowels.

31 20 and 04. Each number is the alphanumeric value of a letter. The words horizontally are: Toad, Goat, Road and Boar.

32 M. A and K are made up of 3 straight lines, T and V are made up of 2, and M and W are made up of 4.

33 Carrot, Turnip, Potato and Pepper. Pepper is the odd one out as all of the others are root vegetables.

34 D.

35 15. ◯ = 2 ◉ = 3 ○ = 4

36 EE. Each two letters are the last two in the spelling of each number up to seven.

37 Sydney 11.07 and Tokyo 8.07. The number of consonants plus the number of letters in the place, then the number of vowels plus the number of letters.

38 10. The number of straight 'lines' in each letter added together.

39 A. Going down each column, each dot is followed by three spaces.

40 K. C is the 3rd letter of the alphabet. Then move on by 6 to I, move on by 9 to R, 12 to D, and so on...

41 E. The object turns 90 degrees clockwise, the end is removed, and the internal object becomes the opposite tone.

42 O. Each person's bloodgroup is the letter that comes directly before the first letter of their name, in the alphabet.

43 5. Add the first four numbers together and divide the result by the last number, to find the answer.

44 New Zealand and South Korea.

45 D. A is the same as B, C is the same as E, F is the same as G.

46 3. Each two columns add up to 38.

47 4th. The number of vowels in the name give its finishing position.

48 Plymouth.

49 4. 7 – 1 + 5 – 4 = 7.

50 'He who laughs last, laughs loudest.' If two alphabets are listed next to each other but with the second beginning at J, then A is J, B is K, S is B and T is C etc.

51 160. Add together the two top numbers, then add together the two bottom numbers and multiply the two totals.

52 Germany.

53 17. The value of the van is 3, the car is 9, and the bike is 5.

54 46ft. The alphanumeric values of the first and last letters in the tree's name added together.

55 8. Add the three numbers together, then add the two digits in that total together.

56 3. The number of consonants in the word.

57 £69,000.

58 12. In each vertical column the vowels are worth 0, and the consonants the same as the column number.

59 Nicholas Cage, Michael Caine, Harrison Ford, Will Smith and Bruce Willis. They are all American, except for Michael Caine.

60 Pall Mall.

61 70. Circle multiplied by the square, and the result multiplied by the star.

62 £60. Take the number of letters in the smaller word away from the number of letters in the larger word, then add a nought.

63 37. Add the two numbers in each circle and move on by that amount.

64 1376. Firstly the total number of letters in the whole name, then the last name, then the Christian name.

65 K. It is midway in the alphabet between each set of two letters.

66 Cable car.

67 102. Multiply the two digits in each number together and move on by that amount.

68 'The post arrives at seven thirty a.m.' Take the last 13 letters in the alphabet and place them below the first 13. Then swap each letter in the code with the one above or below it.

69 C.

70 13. $2 \times 7 = 14$, $1 + 4 = 5 + 8 = 13$.

71 3rd May. May is the fifth month. Each date is the alphanumeric value of the fifth letter of each person's name.

72 A. Each spiral reduces by 90 degrees each time.

73 Belgium. Each person's name ends with the same letter as their favourite country.

74 72.

75 A.

76 12. Moving clockwise from the top middle, the numbers increase by three each quarter. Moving clockwise from the top left, they increase by two each quarter.

77 Portsmouth, Wolverhampton, Edinburgh and Nottingham.

78 72. 117 is divisible by 9. 72 is the only satellite divisible by 9.

79 B. Each shape in the sequence contains one more enclosed space than the one before it.

80 39. Add together the alphanumeric values of the middle two letters.

81 gillian@11315.co.uk. Each set of numbers are made up of the alphanumeric values of the last 3 letters in the surname, in reverse order.

82 1, 4, 7 and 12. Step only on shapes with an even number of sides.

83 5.10. The hands move on 1 hour 30 minutes, then back 40 minutes, and so on...

84 10 miles. Multiply the number of consonants in each destination by the number of vowels.

85 D.

86 Iran. The number of consonants in the place name correspond to the number of consonants in the month.

87 10. The alphanumeric value of the first letter, T, then the next but one letter, the next but two, the next but three and then four.

88 1. The alphanumeric value of the second letter in the opposite hobby.

89 Rangoon. In each case, the first letter in the name of the stopover is the next but one letter in the alphabet to the first letter in the destination.

90 D.

91 58.

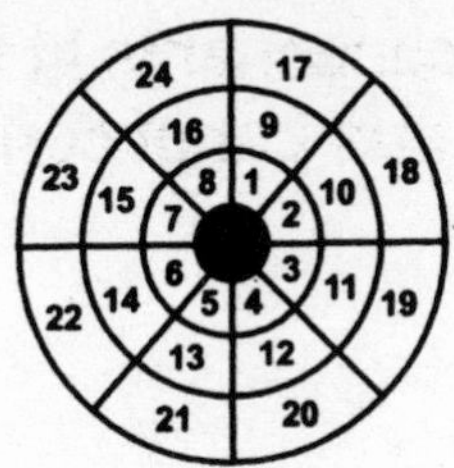

92 16,000 copies. The alphanumeric values of the first letter of each word in the title added together, with the noughts added on.

93 14. Each number is made up of the total number of sides of all the shapes, minus the number of sides in that individual shape.

94 L. The alphanumeric number of each vowel is counted in from the end of the alphabet.

95 7 miles. The number of consonants in the name of the opposite destination.

96 Labrador.

97 11. Each number is the alphanumeric value of the top letter in each circle, the other numbers are irrelevant!

98 B. It should read 2444. Each number is double the alphanumeric value of each letter.

99 55. The first number in each circle is multiplied by 3, then you move on by the result.

100 Top number 1 and bottom 4. Each outer number is halved and moved 90 degrees clockwise round the circle.